MW00628678

from

Joseph & Theresa Smith
Paquette Avenue
Manchester, New Hampshire
03 104

enjoy

# SURVIVAL SKILLS HANDBOOK

## VOLUME 3

EXTREME ENVIRONMENTS

•

WINTER

•

SUMMER

•

WEATHER WATCHING

# CONTENTS

## WINTER

## SUMMER

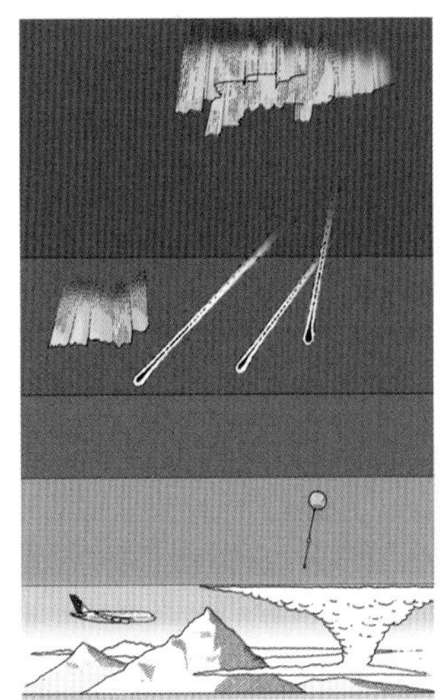

## WEATHER WATCHING

# INTRODUCTION

From the poles to the tropics, our planet has so many incredible places to discover. While there are plenty of places to take a gentle, easy hike in the great outdoors, some people, myself included, love to explore some far more extreme environments. Whether you're hiking across a baking hot desert, discovering the fascinating wildlife of a rain forest, racing down a river on a raft, or trying your hand at dog sledding through the snow, there's so much out there to experience. In these places, you have to be even more careful than normal, as quick-changing weather can be very dangerous, and knowing what to do if the weather turns could be a matter of life and death. This handbook is packed full of tips and tricks to help you stay safe when exploring extreme environments and risky climates, as well as teaching you to understand our planet's ever-changing weather. So what are you waiting for? Get out there and explore!

# EXTREME ENVIRONMENTS

Our planet is full of incredible environments with extreme conditions. Some plants and animals have evolved to live there, but surviving in these places is a struggle. If you want to explore an extreme area, it's vital that you do some serious planning to keep you safe on your adventures!

Bear

# IN THIS SECTION:

# EXTREME EXPEDITIONS

Earth's most extreme environments include deserts, rain forests, mountains, the open ocean, and the polar regions. These wildernesses are often far from civilization, so you'll need to hone your survival skills to stay safe and healthy there.

## Extreme conditions

Most extreme places have a very harsh climate—either freezing cold or boiling hot. Fresh water may be scarce, and features such as cliffs and ice may present hazards. There may be dangerous predators. Hostile conditions mean that very few people live in these regions, so you need to rely on yourself and the other members of your group.

## Clothing

You will need clothing suited to your particular destination, but in general, several thin layers are better than one thick layer. This allows you to adjust your body temperature by taking layers on and off. Pack rainwear unless visiting a desert. Headgear protects you from sun, rain, or cold. Make sure boots are well fitting and comfortable before embarking on any adventure.

## Essential gear

These items will be useful on all expeditions.

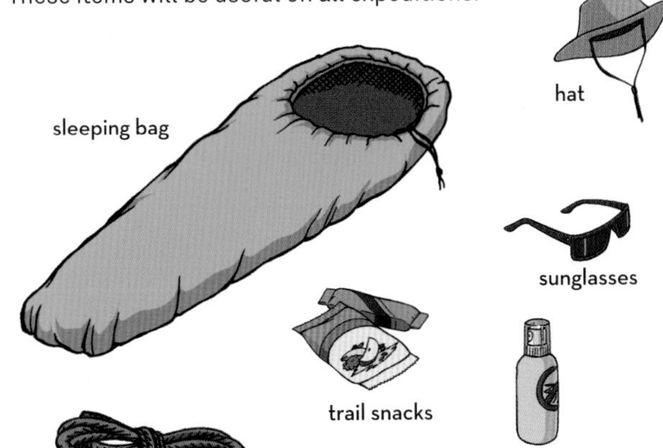


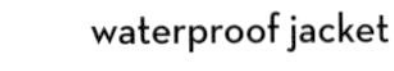


sunglasses

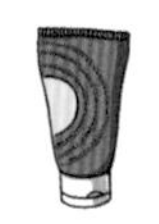


insect repellent

## Mini survival kit

A mini survival kit containing matches, fire steel, flashlight, needle and thread, fishing line, duct tape, string, pocket knife, superglue, and safety pins could save your life in an extreme environment, or even close to home!

**BEAR SAYS**

**Pack your rucksack in reverse order, so the things you need first are on top. Stow useful items such as your map and compass in the pockets, so you can reach them easily.**

# PREPARATION AND GEAR

Thorough preparation is vital for survival in extreme places. Research the climate and conditions and choose equipment carefully. Craft detailed plans and start training for your trip well in advance.

## Camping and cooking

A good tent, sleeping bag, and sleeping pad will keep you comfortable overnight.

## Expedition food

You will need a cooking kit and food supplies to last the expedition—wild foods may be available, but you have to be sure to identify them correctly. Camp stores should supply a healthy balance of carbohydrates, proteins, and fats. Fresh fruit and vegetables provide minerals and vitamins. Dried and canned foods last for a long time, but canned foods are heavy.

**BEAR SAYS**

**Check that everything is in working order before you leave. If you have new gear, read the instructions and make sure you know how it works. If camping, practice putting up and taking down your tent.**

## Signaling and navigation

A navigation kit will help you find your way in the wilderness, while signaling equipment will allow you to communicate with group members and call for help in an emergency. Make sure you take batteries and/or solar chargers for all equipment.

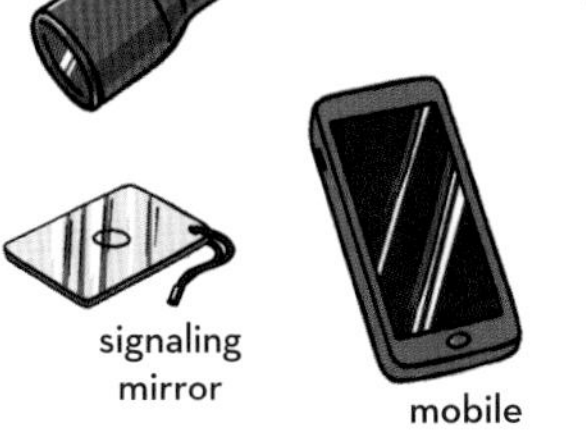


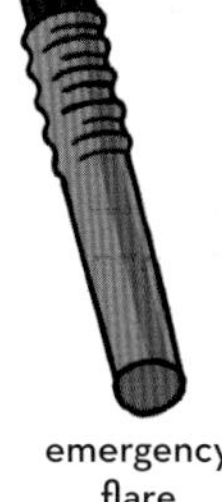


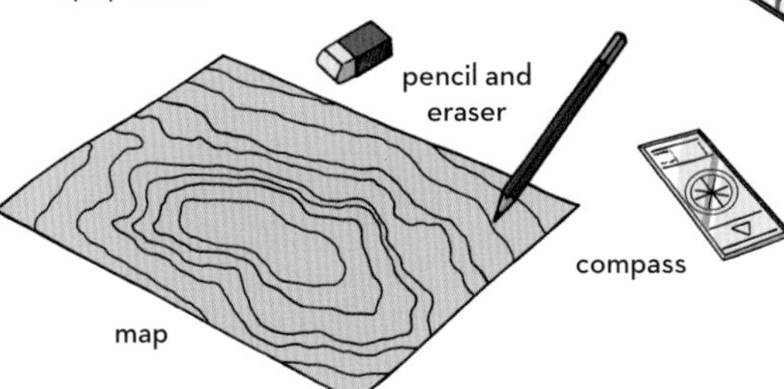


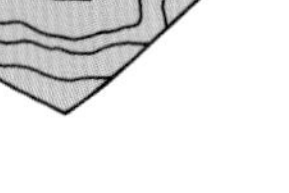

## Guides

Many expeditions to remote places hire a guide to lead the way, advise on local conditions, and identify wild foods. If you don't hire a guide, take a guidebook!

## Planning

Make a detailed timetable for the expedition, including the journey there and back. Make an Emergency Plan of Action (EPA) in case things go wrong. Tell someone where you are going or leave a copy of your plan with them. Include details and contact numbers for all group members.

## Training

Aim to build up stamina for the activities involved on your expedition. For example, go on practice hikes, gradually increasing the distance.

# NAVIGATION

Extreme regions have few trails, and some places are entirely unmapped. It's vital to brush up on your map and compass skills before setting off for a remote place.

## Maps and symbols

Maps use symbols to show features such as paths, rivers, forests, and buildings. However, not all maps use the same symbols. Check the key (legend) at the side of the map to find out what each symbol means.

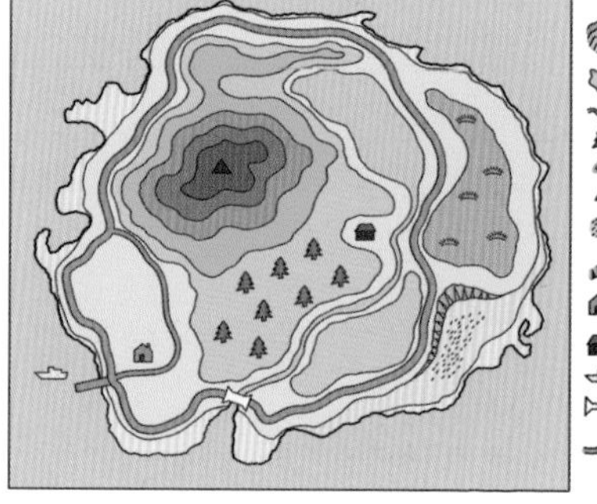


contour lines

## Contour lines

Some maps show the ups and downs of the landscape using lines called contours. These lines link places at the same height above sea level. If the lines are close together, you know the area will be steep.

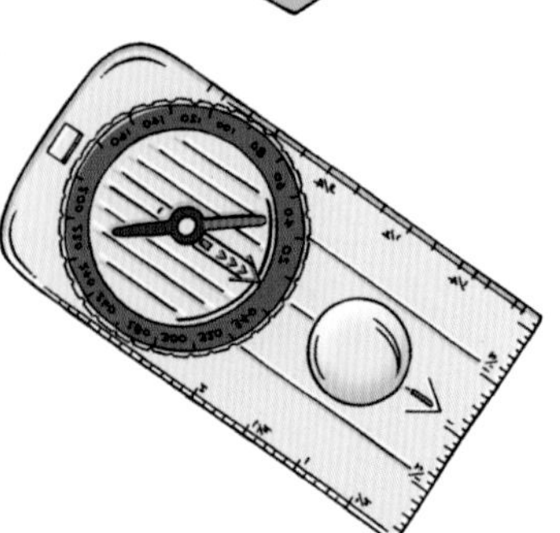

## Compass

The red magnetic needle on a compass always points north. Knowing this, you can work out other directions. You can use a compass in several ways. For example, look at the map to see if your destination lies north, south, east, or west of your current position. Then consult your compass to work out which way to head.

**If you don't have a map, make your own! Head for a high point, such as a hill, and survey the landscape. Mark hills, buildings, and other features. Use a compass to find north, and mark it on your map.**

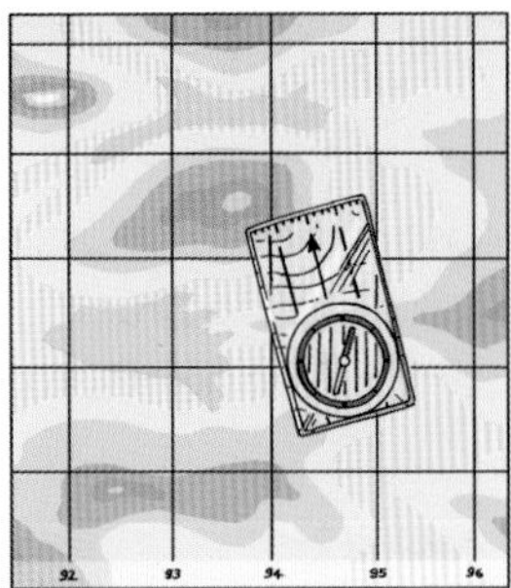


## Map grids

Many maps have a grid of lines, which can be used to pinpoint locations. Grid references give the east-west distance first, then north-south.

## Map scales

Maps are drawn to different sizes—this is called the scale. A map may show a large region in little detail, or a small area in more detail. Knowing the scale can help you to work out how long a journey will take.

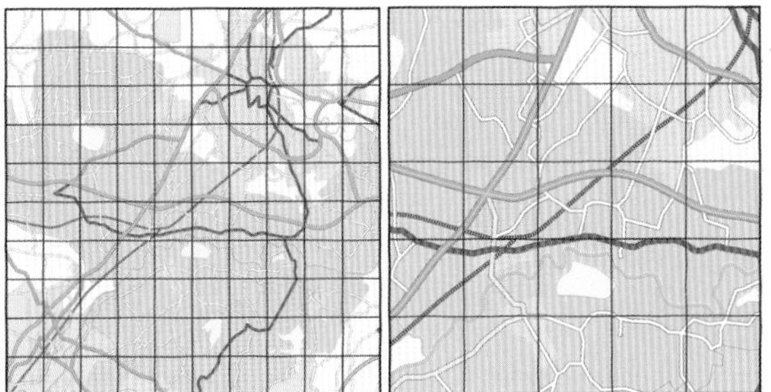

1 inch = 1 mile (1:62,500)

1 2 3 4 5

## Measuring distance

You can measure scale on a map using a piece of string and a ruler. Lay the string along the route you plan to take, then straighten it out and measure it with a ruler to find out the distance.

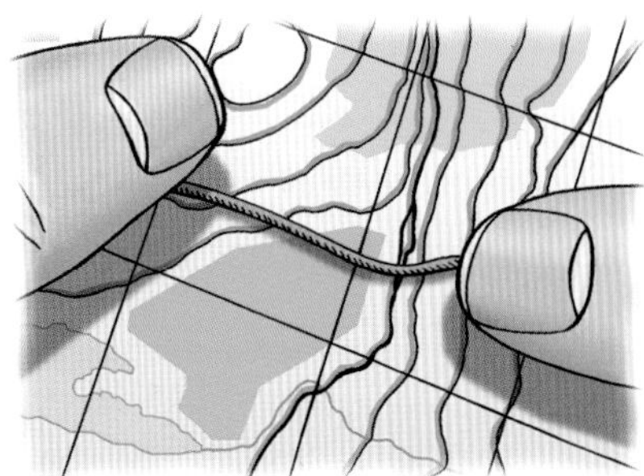

# ESSENTIAL FIRST AID

Wilderness areas are far from hospitals and doctors' offices. All expedition members should know at least basic first aid in order to treat injuries such as cuts, burns, and sprains.

## First aid kit

Pack a full first aid kit for all expeditions to remote places, containing bandages, dressings, latex gloves, scissors, tweezers, and painkillers.

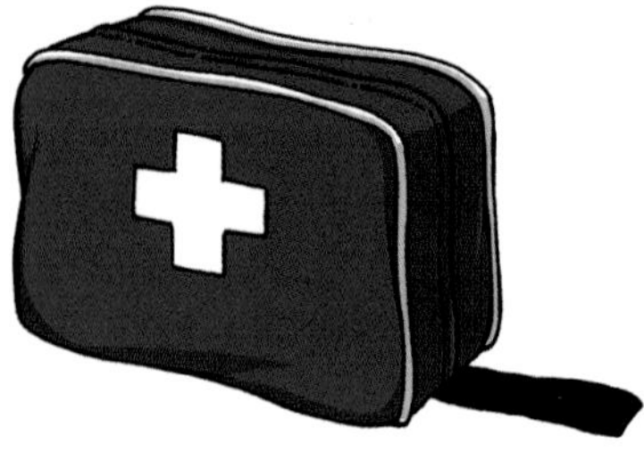

## Bites and stings

A wasp will usually pull its stinger out after it has stung you. If the stinger is left in your skin, remove it with tweezers. Wash and cover with a dressing to keep the wound clean.

## Cuts and grazes

Wash the wound thoroughly and apply antiseptic. Clean wounds from the inside out, or you risk spreading infection. Apply a bandage or dressing to keep the wound site clean.

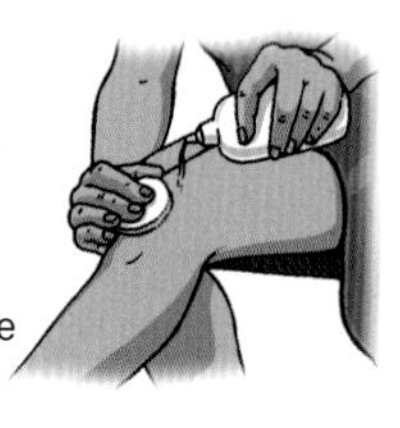

## Treating a snakebite

Prop the victim up to keep their heart above the bitten area. Bandage the whole limb affected, to slow circulation. Keep the patient still, but ask them to describe the snake, so the correct antivenin can be given. Seek medical help immediately.

## Painkillers

These can be bought very easily in drugstores or other shops, and can treat pain such as headaches or sunburn. Make sure to take no more than the recommended dose on the package, and have a responsible adult in charge of handing them out.

## Burns

Run the affected area under cool water for at least 10 minutes. Make sure there is no clothing or jewelry stuck to the burn. Cover the area in plastic wrap or a clear plastic bag to keep it clean. Give the patient plenty of cold drinks.

## Leg injuries

Bandage a sprained ankle. Support a broken leg with a splint, such as a straight stick. Add padding, such as a towel, and secure with an elastic bandage.

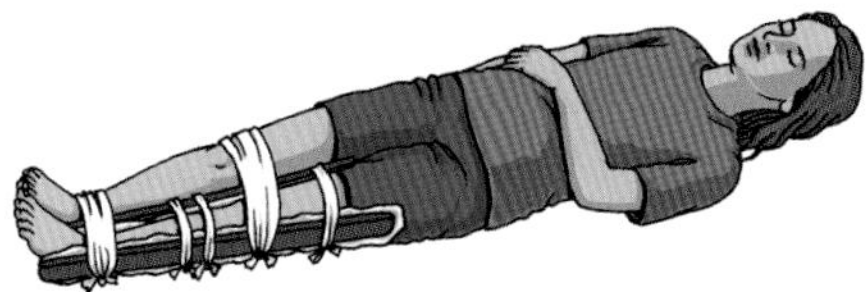

## Broken arms

Support a sprained or broken arm with a triangular cloth tied at the shoulder. You could also use a sweater.

## Recovery position

If the person is unconscious but breathing, roll them onto their side. Move their upper arm and leg outward, and bend their knee and elbow to make the position stable. Place their upper hand beneath their chin to support their head.

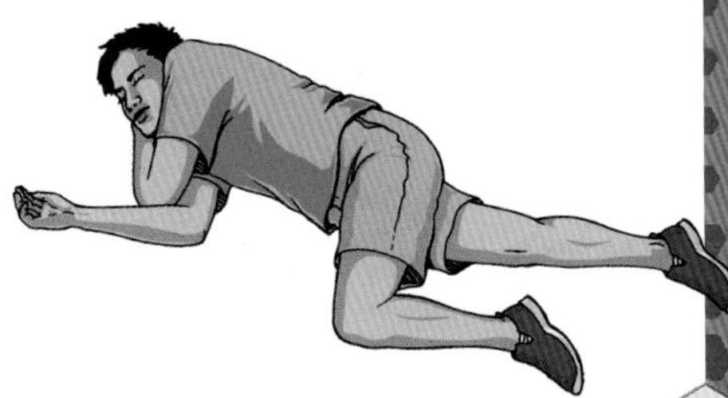

# HOT CLIMATE SURVIVAL

The human body can easily overheat in extreme heat and humidity. The fierce tropical sun can quickly burn your skin, and staying cool and well hydrated will be your main priorities. The tips on this page will help you recognize and treat heat- and sun-related illnesses.

## Heat exhaustion

This is caused by severe heat and humidity, which produces excessive sweating. Symptoms include a weak pulse, dizziness, cramps, and vomiting. Rest the person in the shade with their feet raised. Remove any excess clothing and place cool, wet cloths or cold compresses on their body. Supply cold water with a pinch of salt to avoid dehydration.

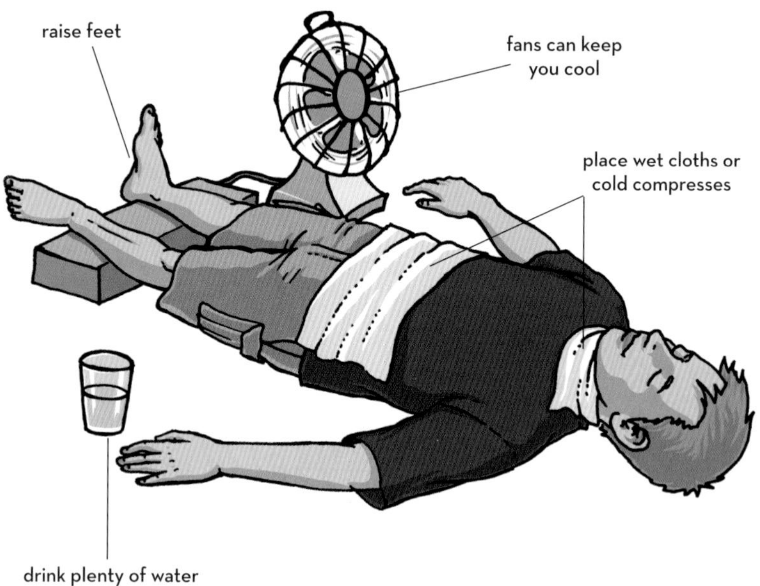

## Heatstroke

Also called sunstroke, this is when the body absorbs heat faster than it can get rid of it. Symptoms include headaches, dizziness, nausea, and vomiting. Rest the patient in the shade. Remove outer clothes and cool the skin with dampened clothing, or cover the person with a damp sheet.

## Sunburn

Sunburn is uncomfortable and can cause skin damage. In extreme cases, the skin may blister. Cool the area with a cold dressing and apply calamine lotion. Prevent sunburn by keeping your skin covered and applying high-factor sunscreen.

**BEAR SAYS**

**Germs breed fast in hot climates. Wounds can quickly turn septic, so take extra care to sterilize cuts and grazes, then cover them to prevent infection.**

## Prickly heat

This uncomfortable skin rash can happen if clothing chafes the skin or excessive sweating blocks sweat glands. Remove clothing, wash the affected area with cool water, and put on dry, clean clothes.

# RAIN FORESTS

Tropical rain forests are one of the toughest environments on Earth. Conditions are hot and humid all year round. Insects will eat you alive, and dense jungle can block your route.

## Dress for the jungle

Wear cotton, or a fabric that absorbs sweat. Fasten clothing at the neck, wrists, and ankles to ward off leeches and biting insects. A poncho will keep you and your rucksack dry during downpours. Put spare clothes in a plastic bag so you have dry things to wear at night.

## Beware poison

Rain forests hold some of the world's most venomous snakes, such as the dreaded fer-de-lance. Hairy spiders called tarantulas have a poisonous bite and can shoot stinging hairs. Poison arrow frogs have deadly toxins in their skin to ward off attacks.

## Dangerous beasts

Some of the world's most powerful predators hunt in jungles. Big cats, such as tigers and jaguars, go after prey as large as deer. African and Asian rain forests are home to elephants and rhinos, which may charge if they feel cornered.

## Avoid getting lost

Hire a local guide, if possible. Otherwise, stay on the trail. It's easy to lose your bearings when dense jungle screens the view in all directions. If separated from your group, stay where you are and shout for the others to come back for you.

## Removing botfly

Botflies lay their larvae on mammals, and the larvae burrow into the host's flesh. Smear petroleum jelly over the wound to suffocate the maggot. Squeeze the sides of the wound, then grasp the tail with tweezers and gently pull the maggot out.

## BEAR SAYS

**Be careful where you tread. Don't step over fallen trees—climb on top and check for snakes coiled on the far side. Never put your hand into a nook or cranny that could hide a poisonous minibeast.**

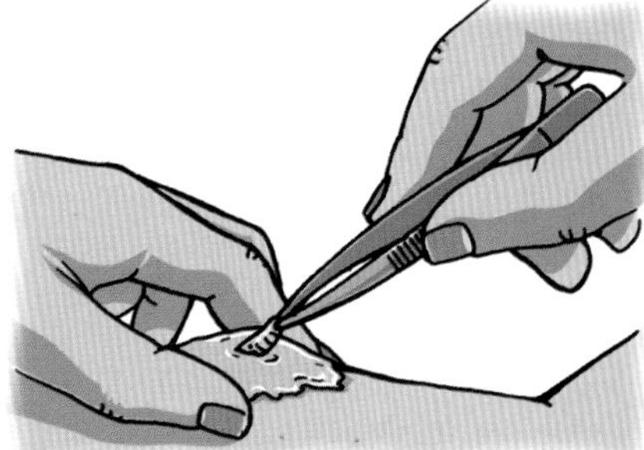

# RAIN FOREST SURVIVAL

To survive for any time in a rain forest, you will need to collect water and light a fire. It will also help if you can source jungle foods, build a shelter, and learn to use a machete so you can clear a route.

### Collecting rainwater

Rain falls almost daily in a rain forest. Rig a tarp between trees or four stakes, as shown, to collect rainwater, or place a container where water pours off your tent. Boil all water before drinking it to kill any dangerous bacteria.

### Tapping into a vine

Some jungle vines hold water. Chop through a vine with a machete, and place a container beneath to catch the flow. Don't drink if the juice is milky.

### Jungle foods

Breadfruit and yams can be cooked and eaten. Look out for bananas, mangoes, figs, and coconuts. Palm shoots and hearts can be eaten raw. Avoid fungi, as many kinds are poisonous.

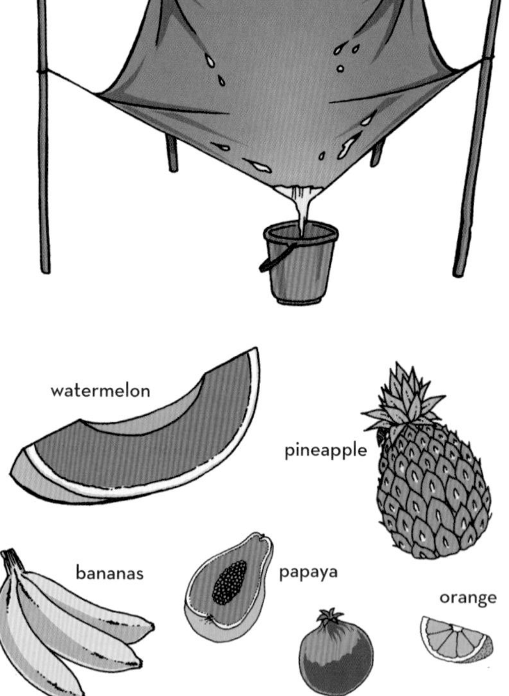

## Rigging a shelter

Always sleep off the ground, out of reach of creepy-crawlies. Sling your hammock between trees and tie it securely. Rig a mosquito net over it. Now string a rope above at head height and throw a tarp or fly sheet over it. Attach guy ropes and tie them to trees or peg them into the ground.

## Using a machete

If there is no trail, you will need to hack your way through with a machete. Take care not to hit anyone as you swing your arm back. Take turns to lead with the machete, as this work is very tiring.

## Communication

Jungle explorers communicate using radios or satellite phones. Mobile phones are no use without a signal. In an emergency, light a signal fire in a clearing, or on a raft tied mid river, so the smoke will rise above the canopy.

**BEAR SAYS**

**Damp conditions make fire lighting tricky. Collect any dry tinder you see. Build a fire platform by laying two layers of logs crosswise, to raise your fire off the damp ground.**

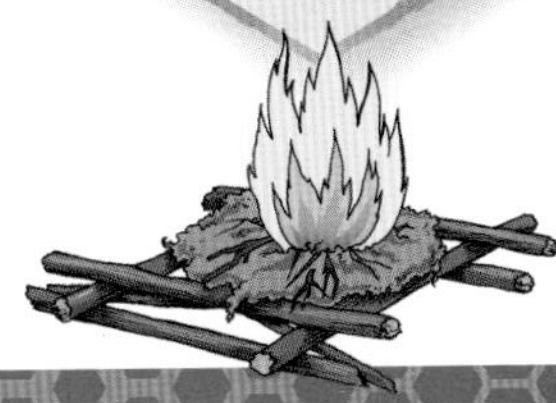

# DESERTS

Deserts have extreme temperatures—scorching hot by day, but falling to around freezing at night. It is also very dry, with less than 10 inches of rainfall per year. You can easily suffer heatstroke or sunburn in these conditions, but the main danger is lack of water.

## Dressing for the desert

Wear light, loose-fitting clothing. Long-sleeved shirts and pants protect you from sunburn. Attach a cloth to a wide-brimmed hat or cap to protect your neck. Wear boots to guard against scorpions. Nights in the desert are cold, so bring warm clothing, a fleece hat, and a blanket.

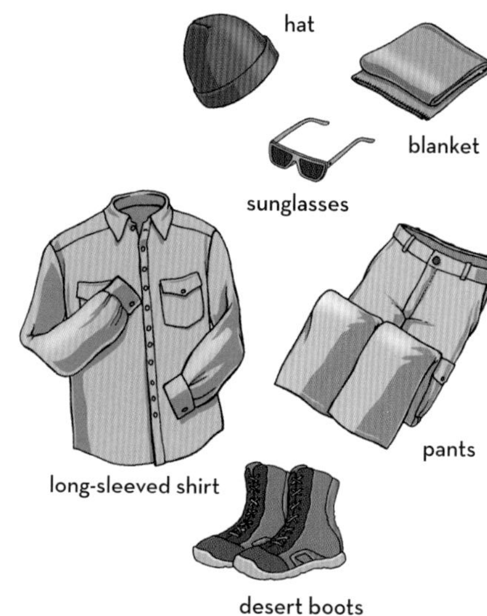

**BEAR SAYS**

**Conserve water by avoiding strenuous activity by day. Rest in the shade during the hottest part of the day, and work or travel by night or at dusk and dawn.**

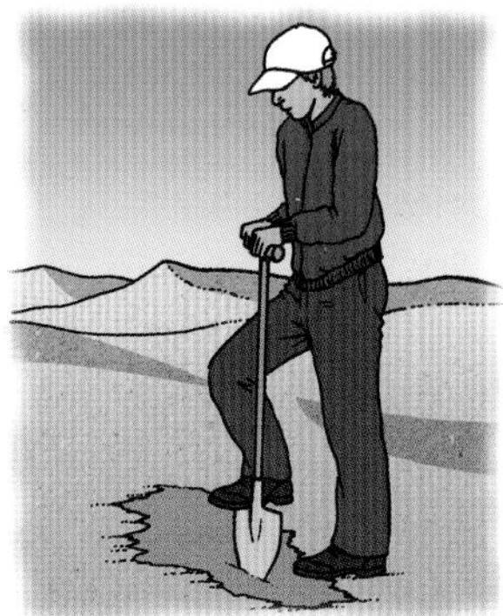

## Searching for water

You need to drink about 2 liters of water a day to top up the body fluids lost through sweating. Bring generous supplies, and scan the map for wells and water holes where you can fill up. Water may also be found by digging down into a dry river bed. Search for greenery on a cliff, as greenery needs water to survive.

## Harvesting dew

Dew forms when warm, moist air condenses on a cold surface. Dig a shallow pit and line it with plastic. Place clean stones on top. Dew will trickle down to the plastic. Harvest the water in the early morning before it evaporates.

## Desert fruits

Prickly pear fruit can be crushed to a wet pulp to provide liquid. Wear gloves when handling this prickly fruit. The fruit and growing tips of date palms can be eaten, as can carob fruit.

## Snakes and scorpions

Desert snakes and scorpions are armed with poison. However, they are wary of humans and will only strike if threatened. Rattlesnakes rattle the loose scales on their tail as a warning. Take care when reaching into crevices and overturning stones.

# DESERT SURVIVAL

The desert climate is harsh. A drought that has lasted for years may be broken by a violent rainstorm, which brings its own dangers. You need to shelter from the sun and sandstorms whipped up by high winds.

## Sandstorms

In a sandstorm, strong winds fill the air with sand and gravel. Be alert for dark clouds on the horizon. If you spot this telltale sign, quickly find shelter, such as a vehicle or rocky outcrop. Wear goggles to protect your eyes and clamp a damp cloth over your mouth and nose.

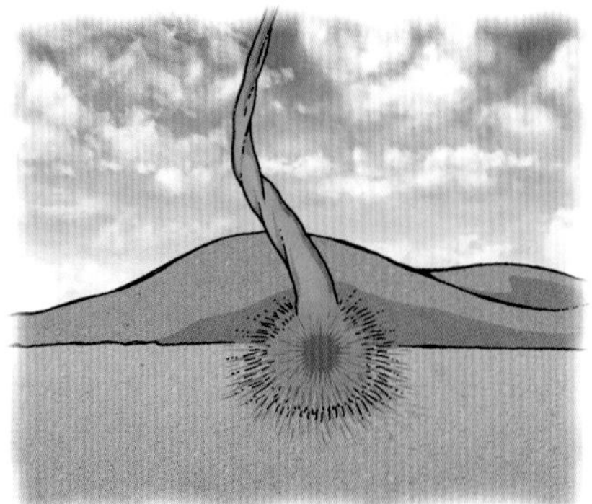

## Dust devils

These are dust-filled whirlwinds caused by rising air. They only last for a few minutes, but could rip your tent to shreds if they catch you off guard.

## Mirages

If you spot a distant pool of water in a desert, it may be a mirage. These optical illusions are caused by light shimmering above hot ground, creating a reflection of the sky.

## Fire lighting

Light a fire at night for warmth and to cook on. Fuel wood will be scarce in a desert, so collect any you pass. Thorn bushes and animal dung can also be burned.

## Emergency signals

Ground-to-air signals work well in a desert. In an emergency, you can use stones or branches to write "SOS" in large letters. You can also use ground-to-air code to communicate with planes.

### BEAR SAYS

**Don't camp in a dry gully if a storm is likely. Rainwater draining off the land will quickly fill these gullies, forming a raging torrent that could sweep away your tent.**

all well

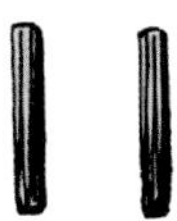

require medical help

require food and water

safe to land

## Building a cordless scrape

1. Dig a pit in the ground, long and deep enough to lie in. Spread a tarp or sheet on top and weigh it down with rocks. Pull it taut.
2. Rig a second sheet above the first, using stones to lift it at least 6 inches above the first sheet. This allows air to circulate.

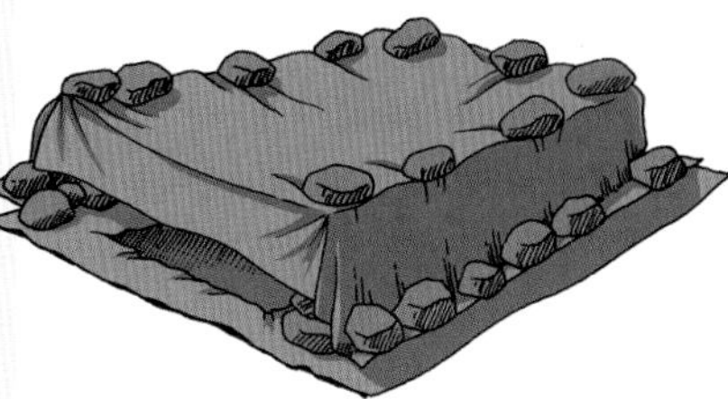

# COLD CLIMATE SURVIVAL

Extreme cold is just as dangerous as heat. Freezing temperatures bring risks of hypothermia and frostbite. Dazzling snow can cause snow blindness. The tips here will help you recognize the symptoms of these conditions and take action.

## Cold climate clothing

You will need several layers of warm clothing, including thermals that absorb sweat. Take a jacket with a fur-lined hood, a balaclava or warm hat, and several pairs of gloves and socks. You will also need goggles and high-factor sunscreen, as the glare of the sun against snow can be damaging to your skin and eyes.

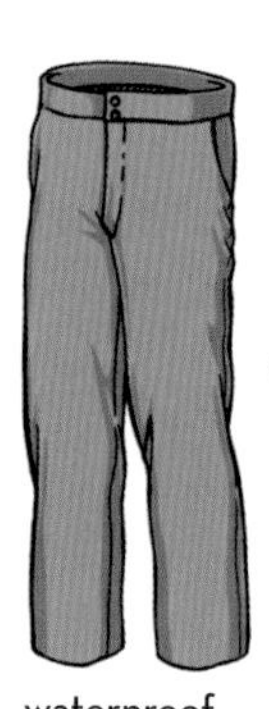

waterproof pants

waterproof jacket

snow goggles

balaclava

thermal so

waterpro
gloves

glove line

thermal bottom layer

## Hypothermia

This happens when your body temperature drops dangerously low—below 95°F. It most often strikes when you are wet, cold, and exhausted. Symptoms include shivering, slow reactions, and poor coordination. The remedy is warming up. Get to shelter, remove wet clothing, and put on dry gear. Wrap up in a blanket or sleeping bag and get some hot food and drinks.

## Frostbite

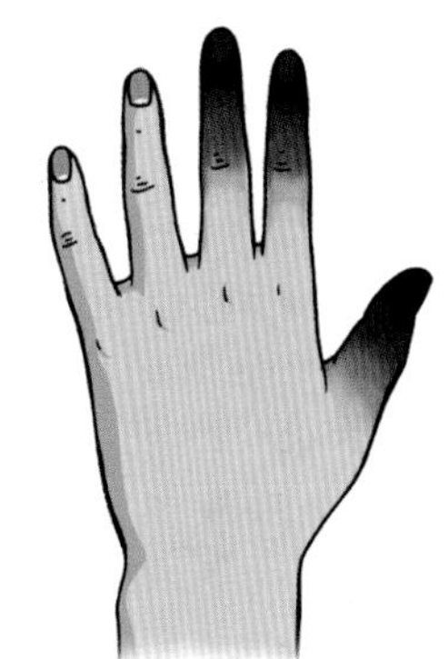

Exposed skin can start to freeze in very cold conditions. Areas most at risk include the nose, ears, toes, and fingers. Cover all exposed skin, including the face. Pair up to watch for the early signs of frostbite, called frostnip—pale, waxy skin which feels prickly, then goes numb. Treat frostnip by immersing the affected part in lukewarm water until feeling returns. Bandage up and seek medical help.

## Windchill

Wind blows heat away from your body, making temperatures feel even colder. The tables below show how windchill affects temperature—the stronger the wind, the more powerful its effect.

| Wind speed mph | Actual temperature °F: 40 | 30 | 20 | 10 | 0 |
|---|---|---|---|---|---|
| 15 | 22 | 9 | -4 | -18 | -31 |
| 20 | 18 | 4 | -10 | -24 | -39 |
| 25 | 15 | 1 | -14 | -29 | -44 |
| 30 | 13 | -2 | -17 | -33 | -48 |

| Wind speed km/h | Actual temperature °C: 4 | -1 | -7 | -12 | -18 |
|---|---|---|---|---|---|
| 24 | -5 | -13 | -21 | -28 | -35 |
| 32 | -7 | -16 | -23 | -31 | -39 |
| 40 | -9 | -17 | -26 | -34 | -42 |
| 48 | -11 | -19 | -28 | -36 | -45 |

**Your outer layer of clothing should not be waterproof unless it's snowing or raining. A non-breathable waterproof layer traps sweat, which then cools and chills.**

## Snow blindness

In snowy landscapes, sun reflecting off white surfaces can cause temporary blindness. Wear goggles or wrap-around sunglasses. In an emergency, improvize goggles from hide, plastic, or cardboard. Cut narrow slits for eyeholes and fasten with elastic, tape, or string.

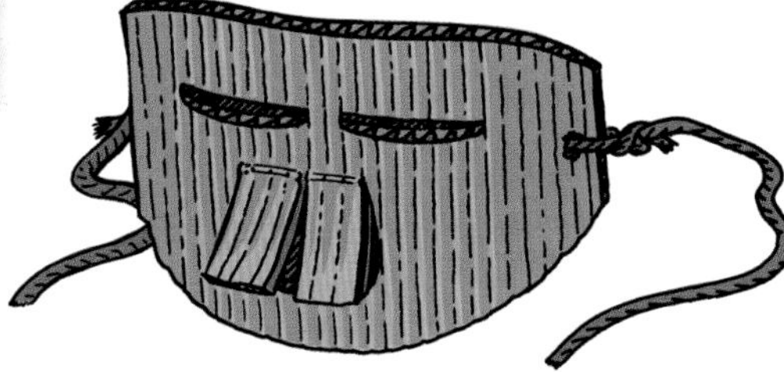

# POLAR REGIONS

The far north and south of our planet are the very coldest places on Earth. Most land here is permanently buried under thick snow and ice. Temperatures plunge far below freezing and hurricane-force winds produce blizzards.

## Polar seasons

The polar regions experience the most extreme seasons on Earth. During long, bitterly cold winters, the sun never rises above the horizon. During the brief summers it is still cold but light for 24 hours a day.

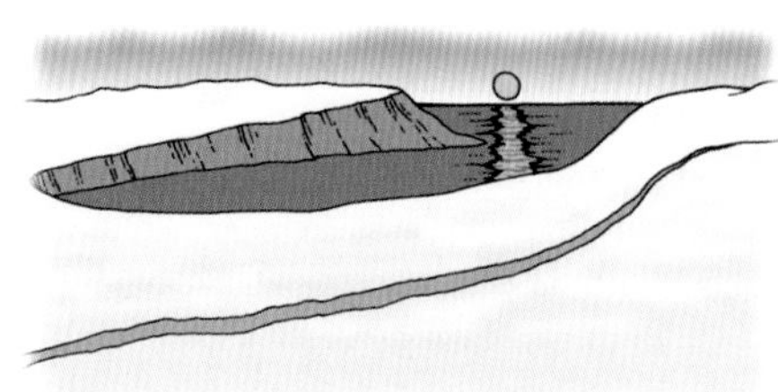

## Arctic

The Arctic region consists of an ice-covered ocean surrounded by the most northerly parts of Europe, Asia, and North America. Most land here is permanently covered by ice, but in the south, snow melts in spring to reveal the treeless lowlands of the tundra (shown left), dotted with pools and bogs.

## Antarctic

The vast, icy continent of Antarctica is covered by an ice cap up to 2.5 miles thick. The coldest temperatures on Earth are recorded here. No plants or animals live inland, but seals and penguins inhabit the coasts.

## Blizzards

A blizzard strikes when high winds combine with falling snow. Whirling snowflakes fill the air, reducing visibility to zero. Prepare for a blizzard by stringing ropes between tents so you can find your way in an emergency. Go outside only when you have to, for example, to dig your tent out of a snowdrift.

## Thin ice

Thin ice is very dangerous. Always check if ice will bear your weight before stepping onto it. If you fall through, swim to the edge, kick strongly, and haul yourself out. Use a pole, branch, rope, scarf, or life jacket to rescue someone who has fallen through the ice.

## Icebergs and floes

In winter, polar seas are ice covered. During the brief summer, sea ice melts and cracks, creating loose chunks called floes. These can tip over if you step on them. Icebergs are a menace to ships—only the tip of an iceberg shows above the surface.

# POLAR SURVIVAL

Imagine camping inside a huge freezer—that's how cold it is in the polar regions. Tasks such as finding food and water, lighting a fire, and even pitching a tent are a challenge in ultra-cold conditions.

## Fire lighting

You will need to light a fire to melt snow for drinking water. Wood may be scarce, so collect any you see. If possible, build a stick platform to insulate your fire from snowy ground.

## Obtaining water

1. Pack snow into a dense ball, skewer it with a stick, and prop it by the fire.
2. Position a container underneath to catch the drips. You can also fill a sock with snow to filter the water as it melts.

1

2

## Wild foods

Berries are plentiful in the Arctic in fall. Cloudberries and salmonberries can be eaten raw. Lichen, such as reindeer moss, should be cooked before eating. The Arctic is also rich in game, such as hare, beaver, grouse, and duck.

cloudberries

salmonberries

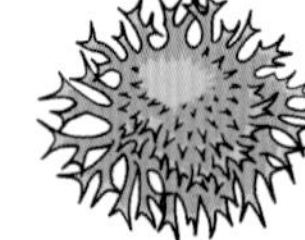

reindeer moss

## Polar predators

Polar bears can scent prey many miles away. These enormous bears are one of the very few creatures that will see you as prey. Walruses are huge members of the seal family. Beware their long, curving tusks, particularly if their young are present.

### BEAR SAYS

**Don't sit on snowy or frozen ground. Use a log, rucksack, sit mat, or bivy bag to insulate yourself from cold ground.**

### Building a snow shelter

You will need: a tarp, a ski or pole, and a trowel.

1. Lay the tarp on the ground and trace around it with your trowel.
2. Cut snow blocks and build walls about 3 ft. high inside the rectangle. Cut a small entrance.
3. Lay the tarp over the shelter, raise the roof with the ski or pole, and anchor with more snow blocks. Cut and fit more blocks to make a porch. Be careful not to pierce the tarp with the pole!

# MOUNTAINS

Conditions high on mountains are similar to the polar regions. Hazards include snow and ice, steep slopes, and lack of oxygen. Mountain weather is very changeable, so stay alert.

### Thin air

The air high on mountains is thinner than it is at sea level. Thin air holds less of the sun's heat, so the temperature drops about 1°F for every 650 ft. you climb. Prepare for wintry, windy conditions on mountain summits.

### Altitude sickness

Thin mountain air also contains less oxygen. This may make you breathless, and strenuous action such as climbing will become much tougher. Lack of oxygen can cause a condition called altitude sickness. Symptoms include dizziness, headaches, and eventually delusion. This condition can be fatal. The only cure is to descend and rest up.

## BEAR SAYS

**Mountaineers avoid altitude sickness by acclimatization. This technique involves gaining height slowly and steadily, and descending a little each night to sleep.**

### Mist and fog

Mist and fog form where the cloud level dips below the mountain summits. When thick mist blots out all landmarks, navigation gets very tricky. You'll need good compass skills to find your way to safety.

## Avalanche danger

An avalanche strikes when a mass of snow and ice breaks loose on a mountain and plunges downhill. Avalanches can be triggered by heavy snowfall, a rise in temperature, or even a passing skier. Beware steep slopes and snow-choked gullies. Use an avalanche pole (below) to check if snow is firm.

### BEAR SAYS

**Mountain weather can deteriorate very quickly. Watch the clouds and seek shelter if you see dark thunderclouds, lightning, or hear distant thunder. Beware of cave entrances in a lightning storm.**

## What to do in an avalanche

If caught in an avalanche, use a swimming movement to stay at the surface. As the avalanche slows, quickly clear a breathing space around your face. If in a group, keep still and calm and wait for rescue. Otherwise, try to punch or kick your way to safety.

# MOUNTAIN SURVIVAL

Mountaineers use safety gear such as helmets, ropes, and crampons. Special techniques are used to scale rock and ice, and cross glaciers. You'll need to master these skills to tackle a serious climb.

## Climbing equipment

As well as cold climate gear, you will need a helmet, rope, and safety harness. Use an ice ax and boot spikes called crampons to grip snow and ice.

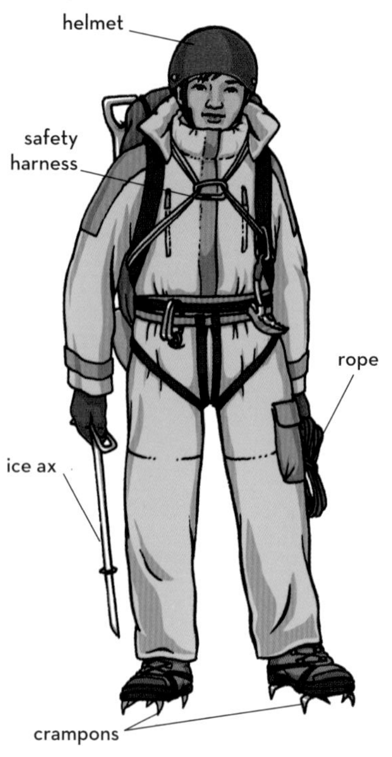

## Going up...

Rope together for steep climbs. Chip steps on snowy slopes with your ice ax. If you start to slip, dig in with an ax or ski pole. You can also anchor yourself by hammering in metal pegs called pitons.

## ...and down

Loop a rope around a secure anchor at the top. Pass the rope around your legs and body. Now turn your back on the drop, lean back with the rope tight, and slowly lower yourself by stepping down while letting out the rope.

## Glaciers

These masses of ice form in hollows high in mountains. As the ice very slowly flows downhill, it splits to form deep cracks called crevasses. Beware rotten ice at the base of a glacier, called the snout.

## Glacier crossings

Rope up for a glacier crossing. Beware crevasses hidden by fresh snow. If someone falls into a crevasse, keep the rope taut while they climb out, or haul them to safety, using ice axes to anchor the rope.

**When climbing up or down a rock face, only move one arm or leg at a time—keep three anchor points on the rock at all times.**

## Making a snow hole

Dig a shelter in a deep drift. Tunnel slightly downhill and then uphill, then hollow out a chamber. Pack down loose snow to make a sleeping platform. Use a pole to make breathing holes in the roof.

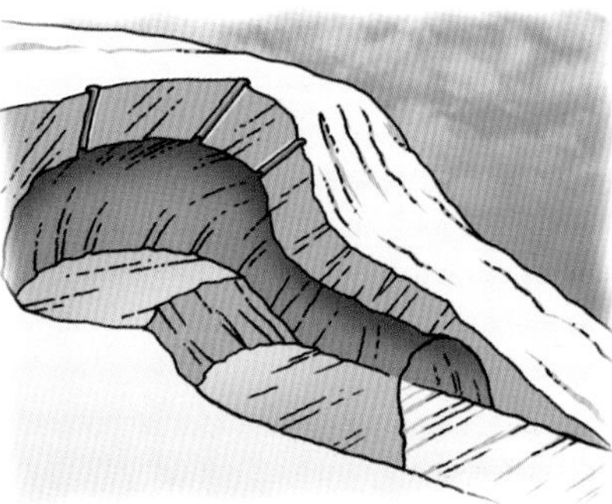

# VOLCANOES

Volcanoes are weak points in the Earth's crust where molten rock, ash, and gas escape from deep underground during an eruption. People settle on the slopes of volcanoes because the soil is fertile, but some volcanoes can erupt without warning.

### Eruption hazards

Eruptions are extremely dangerous. Red-hot lava, toxic gas, and burning ash are all killers. Experts class volcanoes as active, dormant (quiet but potentially active), and extinct (dead). Make sure you're aware of any dormant or active volcanoes before you travel to an area.

## BEAR SAYS

**Only experts approach active volcanoes. They wear protective suits to sample ash, gas, and lava. Heed all warning signs and never abseil into an active or dormant volcanic crater.**

## Other dangers

Some volcanoes erupt quietly, spilling out runny lava. Others explode without warning. Volcanic eruptions can also trigger tsunamis (tidal waves), avalanches, and mudflows that destroy settlements in their path (shown right).

## Island eruptions

Many islands are volcanic. Sudden eruptions here are particularly dangerous as there is nowhere to escape. In 1902, Mount Pelée on the Caribbean island of Martinique erupted suddenly, killing 28,000 inhabitants.

## Warning signs

Experts examine volcanoes for signs that an eruption is due. Molten rock welling up from below can cause mountainsides to bulge. Sulfurous gases may leak out. If experts believe an eruption is imminent, the order to evacuate is given. Obey evacuation warnings immediately and leave swiftly and calmly. Don't stay to pack your things.

## Volcano defenses

There are some ways to slow the flow of lava—professionals may be able to block it with barricades or solidify it with water.

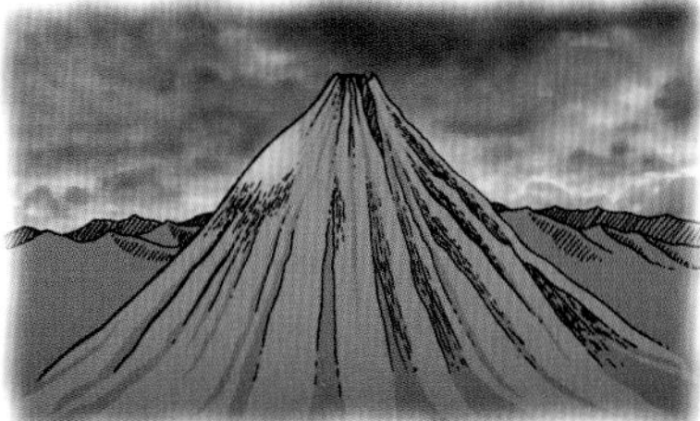

# OPEN OCEAN

The open ocean is an alien environment with very few resources. If a boat accident strands you in open water, you are likely to be fighting for your life. In a situation like this, survival know-how can be a lifesaver.

## Sea survival kit

Don't abandon ship unless you have to. If the order to evacuate is given, put on warm clothing, including a hat and a life jacket. Take candy or trail snacks, a flashlight, and a whistle.

**BEAR SAYS**

**Try to enter cold water gradually. Grab onto floating debris such as a wooden spar or large plastic container. Swim away from a sinking ship.**

life jacket

trail snacks

hat

water bottle

whistle

flashlight

## Survival swimming

Swimming strongly will quickly exhaust you. Tread water to save energy. Hold your body upright and move your legs and arms in slow circles to stay afloat.

## Righting a dinghy

Right a capsized craft by hauling on the ropes as shown in the picture on the left. Work as a team, shouting to coordinate your movements.

## Rough seas

In rough seas, try to meet waves face on and don't get pulled under. Rest with your head in the water once the wave has passed, breathe out, and then briefly raise your head to breathe in.

## Shark attack

The scent of blood attracts sharks. If you spot a shark fin approaching, try not to panic. Make for safety with strong, powerful strokes. If the shark attacks, jab its eyes or nostrils with a pointed object.

## Conserving heat

Water sucks away your body heat. If you are wearing a life jacket, conserve heat by tucking your knees up and crossing your arms. Wear a hat to stop heat escaping through your head.

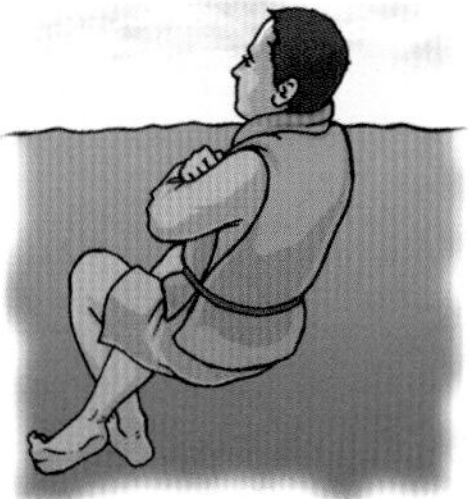

## Make a float

Remove your pants and tightly knot the bottoms of the legs together. Holding the waistband open, sweep the pants over your head to trap air inside. Hold the waistband tightly to your chest and put the legs over your head.

# SURVIVAL AT SEA

You are more likely to survive in a life raft than in the water. However, thirst, hunger, and exposure are still very serious hazards. Keep calm, take stock of your resources, and then take action to secure safety, shelter, water, and food.

## Fresh water

Drinking water is a top priority. Ration all supplies immediately. Spread a tarp to catch rainwater. Collect dew using cloths, which you can then wring into a container. Never drink seawater. Store fresh water in the shade to prevent evaporation. Take care that seawater does not contaminate your supplies.

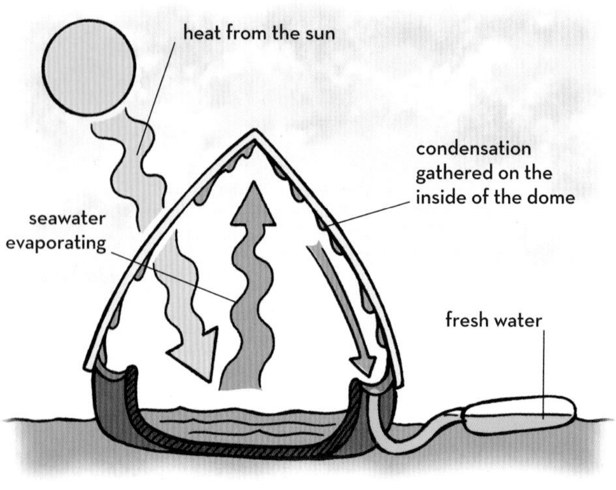

heat from the sun
condensation gathered on the inside of the dome
seawater evaporating
fresh water

## Solar still

This device distills fresh water from seawater. The sun's heat causes seawater to evaporate and condense on the dome's sides. Fresh water trickles down into the container. You can buy these, or make them using a tarp and a clean container to store the water.

## Fishing

Improvise fishing tackle using a nylon line, and a hook, safety pin, or bent nail. Bait the hook and try your luck. Use a flashlight to attract fish at night. Don't fish if there are sharks about.

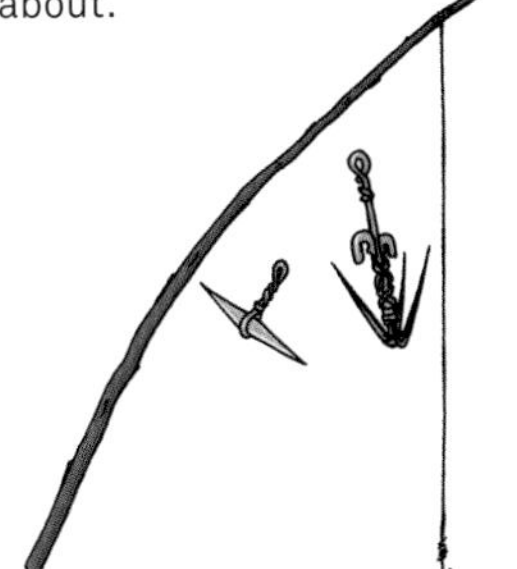

## Gutting a fish

Gut a fish by slitting the belly from tail to gills. Remove guts and use them as bait. Fish eyes are a valuable source of fluid.

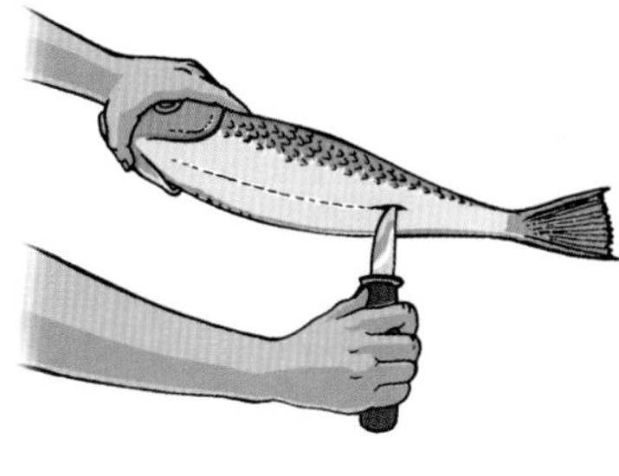

## Signaling for rescue

Some life rafts are equipped with a signaling kit, such as flares, a personal locator beacon (PLB), and a radio. You can use a mirror to flash a ship or aircraft. Be very careful when lighting a flare—direct it away from the raft or it could easily burn a hole.

## BEAR SAYS

**Check the raft for leaks daily. Repair punctures by gluing on rubber patches. Some life rafts are equipped with special plugs to seal leaks. Bail as necessary. In rough seas, tie yourself to the raft.**

## Signs of land

Clouds form over land. Seabirds fly out to sea by day and return in the late afternoon. Beware waves, rocks, and reefs as you approach land.

# FRESHWATER HAZARDS

For centuries, rivers and lakes have been used for travel, particularly in extreme places such as jungles. However, river travel has its perils—beware white water, strong currents, and aquatic predators.

## Gear and clothing

The clothing and equipment you will need depend on the climate and whether you're traveling by canoe, boat, or raft. In general, you'll need a windproof outer layer and light shoes that provide grip. Pack sun protection, a rope, and something to bail with. Stow dry things in plastic bags. Wear a life jacket and helmet for white water.

sunscreen

rope

bucket

helmet

## River hazards

Check the route ahead for dangers such as rapids, weirs, waterfalls, and sandbanks. You'll need to learn special techniques to navigate white water. Rapids form where water flows over submerged rocks. The noise of rushing water can alert you to a waterfall ahead. Look out for hidden sandbanks, which could beach or damage your craft.

## Man overboard!

If you fall overboard, turn so you are heading downstream feetfirst. Brace your feet to take the impact of any rocks. Scan ahead for a place to scramble ashore.

## Flash floods

Heavy rainfall transforms peaceful rivers into raging torrents. The water level can rise very quickly, so camp high above the river.

**BEAR SAYS**

**Check the weather forecast and tide times on a tidal river. Don't overload your craft, and stow all gear securely. Avoid sudden movements that could capsize your craft. Be aware of other water users.**

## Aquatic predators

Some rivers contain dangerous creatures. Crocodiles lie submerged with just their eyes and nostrils showing. Electric eels can deliver a charge of 500 volts—enough to knock you off your feet. Piranhas eat victims with their razor-sharp teeth.

## Portaging a canoe

If you need to pass an obstacle or dangerous patch of water, you can portage your canoe by land. Beach your canoe and scout the route ahead on foot. Tip the canoe upside down as you lift it above your head. Carry your craft beyond the hazard, and then go back for your supplies.

# RIVER CROSSINGS

Streams and rivers can block your way on land. There may be steep, slippery banks, hidden rocks, and strong currents. If the water is too deep for wading, you will need to swim across or turn back and find another route.

## Scouting for crossing points

Scan along the bank for a shallow place to cross. Where a stream narrows or divides it may be possible to leap across. Don't cross on a bend, where the current flows swiftly. Waves and eddies reveal where rocks lie underwater. A fallen tree can form a bridge. Rig a rope between branches for added safety.

## Wading a river

Avoid crossing alone if possible. Find a stout stick to help you balance. Roll your pant legs up, but keep your boots on to grip rocks. Undo the hip belt of your rucksack, and aim slightly downstream.

## Group crossings

Cross as a group in a line, with arms around each other's shoulders. The strongest person should be positioned upstream.

## Crossing with a rope

This technique allows a group of three or more to cross a swift current. You will need a long rope. Only the person crossing should be roped on, with the others paying out the rope.

1. The strongest person should cross first, while others pay out the rope as needed.
2. Once the first person is across, the second should tie onto the rope and cross. Repeat until everyone but one has crossed.
3. The last person should cross while others provide support.

## Floating your gear

Pile your clothes and gear onto a plastic sheet. Add branches and other objects that will float, such as empty plastic containers. Fold the sheet over tightly and secure with rope or string.

### BEAR SAYS

**To improvise a dry bag, put dry clothes and gear in a plastic bag. Squeeze the air out, then fold the top over several times and secure with a clip or rubber band.**

# SEASHORES AND ISLANDS

Seashores offer abundant food such as seaweed, fish, and shellfish. However waves, tides, currents, and marine creatures can be dangerous, even on a calm and sunny beach.

tide in

tide out

## Tides

Tides rise and fall on seashores once or twice a day. Check tide times or watch to find out what the tide is doing. When exploring beaches, be careful not to get cut off by a rising tide. Tides affect offshore currents too—a falling tide can pull you out to sea.

## Opening a coconut

Coconuts are tricky to open. Drive a sharpened stake into one of the "eyes." Drink the milk, then smash the nut to eat the flesh.

## Gathering seafood

Seashores are some of the easiest places to forage for wild food. Catch or net fish, crabs, and shrimp in rock pools. Pry limpets off rocks, or dig down to reach worms and shellfish buried in the sand. Seaweeds such as laver, kelp, and sea lettuce should be boiled before eating.

## Stings and spines

Many sea creatures are armed with poison, stings, or barbs. Blue-ringed octopuses and lionfish are extremely poisonous. A sting from a man-of-war jellyfish can be fatal. Stingrays, triggerfish, and weever fish have sharp dorsal spines.

man-of-war

tingray

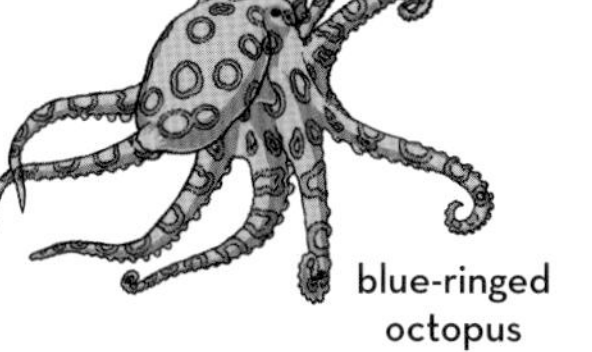

blue-ringed octopus

## Sea-going crocs

Saltwater crocodiles, or "salties," haunt coastal waters, lagoons, rivers, and lakes in Australia and Southeast Asia. These ferocious predators seize prey as large as humans and hold them underwater until they drown.

## BEAR SAYS

**Don't swim alone or in a big surf, which creates a strong undertow. When fishing off headlands, beware crashing waves and slippery rocks.**

# SEASHORE SURVIVAL

Most seashores have plentiful materials to build rafts and shelters. Driftwood is abundant, so you can light a fire to cook or ward off animals. However, fresh water may be scarce.

## Finding fresh water

Collect water from streams rather than salty or muddy estuaries. Ferns and mosses on cliffs reveal the location of streams and springs, but be very careful when near cliffs, and keep an eye out for falling rocks. Always purify water before drinking it.

## Building a shelter

**Scour the beach for materials such as timber and canvas. You will need several long, straightish branches or poles.**

1. Use the longest branch for the ridgepole. Lash securely to trees or to timber A-frames.
2. Lay a pole or log to form the back of the shelter. Lean smaller poles and branches sloping from the ridgepole, and lash securely.
3. Weave palm fronds or smaller branches to make a thatch, or cover with a tarp or plastic sheet.

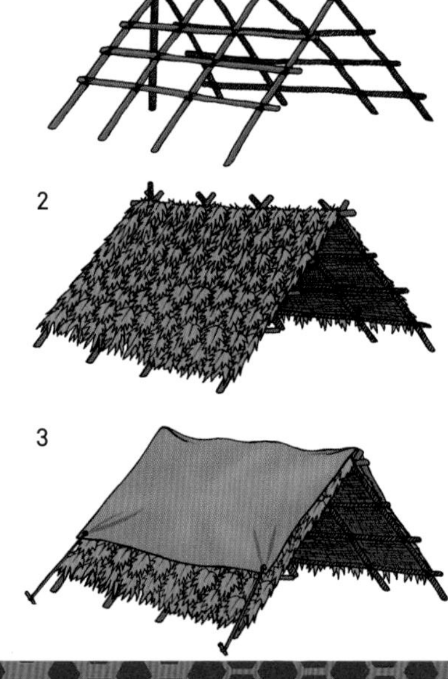

## Building a raft

1. Gather wooden spars and driftwood. Lash several long pieces of wood together with rope, then lash more wood crosswise. Add any floats for extra buoyancy.
2. Test to see if the raft floats and adjust as needed. Rig an upright pole for a mast. Attach a screen of leaves to provide shelter, or canvas for a sail.

## Digging a well

If you have a trowel, you may be able to reach water by digging behind the first sand dune on the beach. Otherwise, watch for approaching storms and position a plastic sheet or tarp to catch rainwater (see page 22).

**BEAR SAYS**

**Check along the high tide mark for useful objects such as containers, bottles, cork, floats, and timber. It can be surprising what washes up on a beach!**

## SOS

In an emergency, write an SOS signal in the sand with sticks, rocks, seaweed, or by drawing letters with a stick. Position your signal above the high tide mark so it doesn't get washed away by the sea!

# WINTER

Winter is an incredible time—it changes the landscape and shows you the natural world in a whole different light! The tips in this section will help you stay safe and warm on any winter expedition. So get ready to discover how to adventure in hostile climates!

Bear

# IN THIS SECTION:

# DRESSING FOR WINTER

Winter is a great season to spend time in the wild and enjoy activities such as hiking, sledding, and skiing. You can also hone your survival skills by camping, making fire, and cooking. However, you have to prepare well to enjoy winter, and that includes dressing for the cold.

## Clothing

Staying warm is your number one priority in winter weather, so it's very important to have the right clothes. You'll need these items of clothing to stay warm in wet or snowy weather.

thick socks

sturdy, waterproof boots

warm hat

gloves and glove liners

long-sleeved base layer

multiple warm layers

## Layer method

Wearing several thin layers is better than one thick layer. Air trapped between the layers provides insulation. The layer method allows you to fine-tune your body temperature by taking a layer off as you warm up, and adding one if you feel cold.

waterproof pants

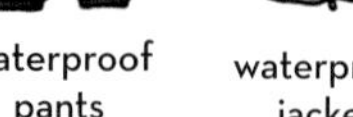

waterproof jacket

**Base layer** Thermals and base-layer clothing absorb sweat.

**Mid layer** Wear breathable fabrics such as cotton.

**Outer shell** Outer layer should be windproof but breathable, so sweat can evaporate. In wet conditions, it should be waterproof.

**Upper layers** Materials such as wool and fleece provide warmth.

## Beware the sun

Ultraviolet light from the sun can cause skin damage. The risk is even greater when sunlight reflects off snowy surfaces. Wear high-factor sunscreen, lip balm, and sun-glasses or goggles to protect your eyes.

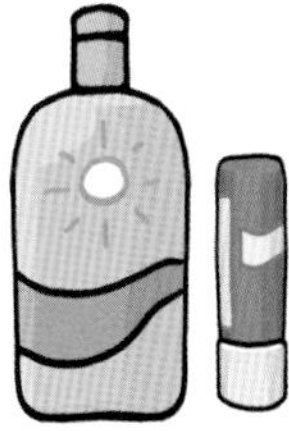

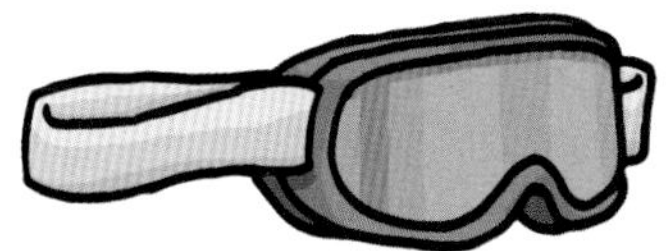

## Gear

Don't forget these important items for outdoor expeditions.

flashlight

mobile phone

water bottle

trail snacks

### C.O.L.D.

**The initials C.O.L.D. spell good advice for winter clothing.**

C Clean clothing is warmer than dirty, as the fibers of clean fabrics trap warm air.

O Avoid overheating and sweating, which can make you colder.

L Loose-fitting clothes allow freedom of movement and good circulation.

D Keep dry—wet clothing will chill your body.

# WINTER WEATHER

Winter brings cold conditions across the temperate regions (areas that have distinct seasons). In some areas, temperatures plunge below freezing. Snow, ice, hail, and blizzards may be hazards. Check the forecast and stay alert to what the weather may bring.

## Snow

Snow forms when floating moisture in clouds freezes to form ice. In certain conditions, ice crystals join to make snowflakes, which eventually get so heavy they fall to the ground. Wind can blow fallen snow into deep drifts.

## Blizzards

Blizzards strike when high winds combine with falling snow. Whirling snowflakes fill the air, reducing visibility to zero—this is called a whiteout. The wind will drive snow into any gaps in clothing, so be sure to zip up tightly before going out.

## Hail

Hail forms when rising winds toss ice crystals up and down inside clouds. Each time a hailstone rises and falls, it gains a fresh layer of ice. Hail can get so heavy it smashes glass and rips tent fabric. If caught in a hailstorm, take shelter while raising your arms to protect your head.

## Windchill

Wind sucks heat away from your body, making temperatures seem even colder. These tables show how wind speeds lower temperature. Avoid exposed, windy places, such as ridges, or gullies and valleys that funnel the wind.

| Wind speed mph | Actual temperature °F 40 | 30 | 20 | 10 | 0 |
|---|---|---|---|---|---|
| 15 | 22 | 9 | -4 | -18 | -31 |
| 20 | 18 | 4 | -10 | -24 | -39 |
| 25 | 15 | 1 | -14 | -29 | -44 |
| 30 | 13 | -2 | -17 | -33 | -48 |

| Wind speed km/h | Actual temperature °C 4 | -1 | -7 | -12 | -18 |
|---|---|---|---|---|---|
| 24 | -5 | -13 | -21 | -28 | -35 |
| 32 | -7 | -16 | -23 | -31 | -39 |
| 40 | -9 | -17 | -26 | -34 | -42 |
| 48 | -11 | -19 | -28 | -36 | -45 |

## Heat conduction

Materials conduct (carry away) heat at different speeds. Metals such as steel conduct heat much faster than wood or plastic. This knowledge is important when using tools, such as knives and shovels, outdoors.

Aluminum—highly conductive

Steel—very conductive

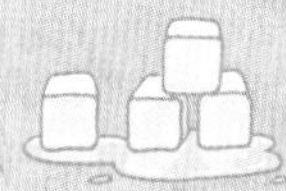

Ice—moderately conductive

Water—quite conductive

Wood—not very conductive

Air—barely conductive

## Mist and fog

Mist and fog are low-level cloud. They can be particularly dangerous on winter journeys when hesitation can quickly make you cold. Pack a compass and know how to use it. With a map and compass, you can find your way even in thick fog.

**BEAR SAYS**

**Stay alert to changing weather on winter expeditions. Rising winds and gathering clouds can mean rain, snow, or hail is on the way.**

# STAYING SAFE

Keeping warm is the main challenge outdoors in winter. In freezing temperatures, you run the risk of hypothermia. Exposed skin can also start to freeze. The answer is to wrap up warm, stay alert, and know what to do if danger signs appear.

## Hypothermia

Hypothermia occurs when your body temperature dips dangerously low. It most often strikes if you are wet, chilled, or exhausted. Symptoms include shivering, tiredness, headaches, confusion, and lack of coordination. If not treated, unconsciousness can follow. Get to shelter as quickly as possible. Remove wet garments one at a time, and replace with dry clothing. Wrap up in a sleeping bag or blanket. Hot food and drinks will help you warm up.

## Frostbite

Frostbite is when skin and flesh start to freeze. Areas most at risk are the "extremities"—ears, nose, toes, and fingers. If possible, pair up to check one another for the early signs of frostbite–when skin turns waxy. Wiggle your fingers and stamp your feet to improve circulation. Treat frostbite by warming the affected part, for example, by placing your fingers in your armpits, or in warm water. Do not rub your cold skin, as this can cause tissue damage.

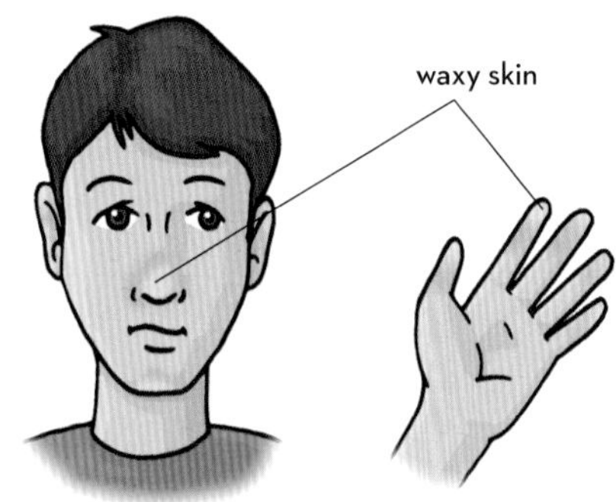

## Snow blindness

Sunlight reflecting off dazzling snow can inflame the eyes, causing temporary blindness. Treat by covering the eyes and resting in a dark place.

## Improvised goggles

Guard against snow blindness by wearing wrap-around sunglasses or goggles. If you have none, you can improvise goggles using a strip of cardboard or leather. Cut narrow slits for eyes and use elastic, string, or even tape to fasten to your face.

## Trench foot

Trench foot can develop if feet are left cold and damp for hours. The feet may feel numb or prickly, and look purplish or swollen. Blisters may develop. Dry and warm the feet and put on dry footwear.

## First aid kit

Pack a full first aid kit for all winter expeditions, including dressings, bandages, painkillers, medical tape, and scissors.

# WINTER HIKING

Winter is a great time to go hiking. However, as for all winter activities, you will need the right equipment and clothing to stay warm and comfortable. This could save your life if accident strikes, or if the weather takes a turn for the worse.

## Clothing and equipment

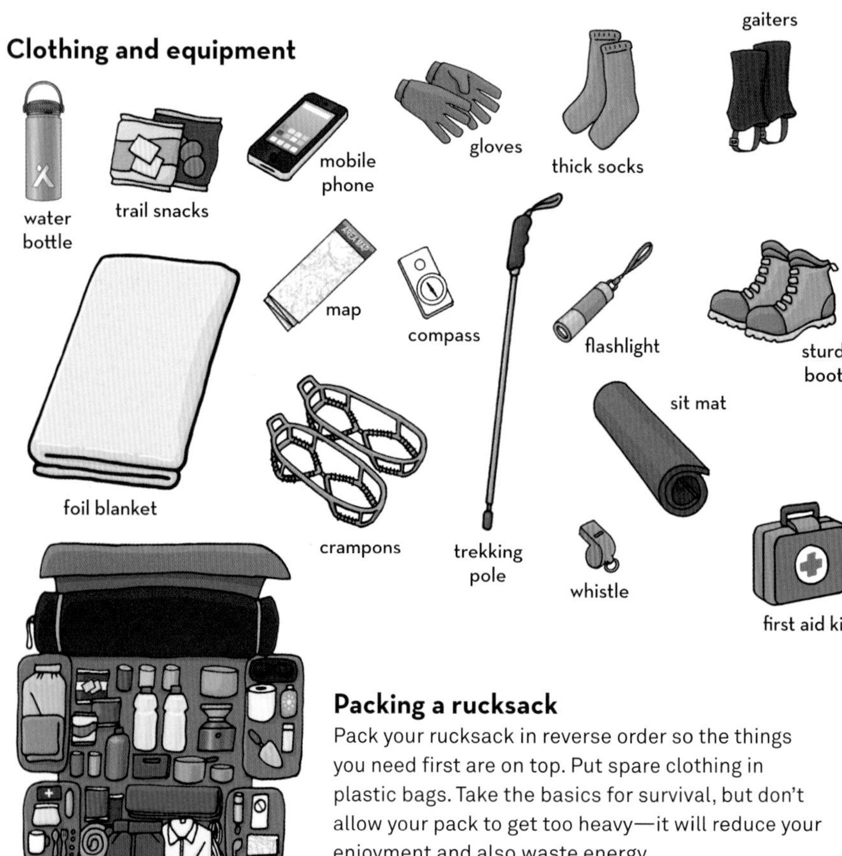


## Packing a rucksack

Pack your rucksack in reverse order so the things you need first are on top. Put spare clothing in plastic bags. Take the basics for survival, but don't allow your pack to get too heavy—it will reduce your enjoyment and also waste energy.

## Plan of action

Check the weather forecast before setting out on a winter hike. Leave a note or tell a trusted adult where you are going and the time you expect to reach your destination. The alarm will then be raised if you don't appear. Include contact details, such as phone numbers, for everyone in the group.

## Navigation

Thick snow blots out trail marks and can hide landmarks. It's all too easy to get lost as even familiar places look different in the snow. Follow the route on the map and make a mental note as you pass landmarks and trail junctions. You could use trail marks such as small cairns to mark crucial turns in the route.

**Don't be overambitious when planning a winter hike. Poor conditions can slow you down. Make a backup plan in case things go wrong—you should prepare for the unexpected!**

## Mini survival kit

A mini survival kit, containing matches or a lighter, candles, a compass, water purification tablets, and basic first aid supplies could be a lifesaver in an emergency situation.

# Hiking techniques

Snow and ice present particular challenges for hikers, and tackling them can be tiring. The tips and techniques on this page will help you move over frozen terrain safely, swiftly, and efficiently, using minimum effort.

## Sticks and poles

A trekking pole or ski pole provides support and stability for winter hiking. One or two poles can help you avoid slipping. You can also use a pole to test the depth of the snow.

## Crampons

Crampons are spikes you attach to your boots to grip snow and ice. You can easily buy mini crampons to fix onto boots.

## Snow hazards

Avoid wading through deep snow if possible—it will soak through your boots and clothes and quickly exhaust you. In icy conditions, a crust may form on the surface, but beware of breaking through to the soft snow underneath. If temperatures rise, snow can start to melt, creating slushy conditions that make the going tough. Warm weather also increases the risk of avalanche (see pages 90–91).

## Breaking trail

Move in single file through deep snow. Walking in the footsteps of the person in front saves energy. "Breaking trail" in front is exhausting, so take turns to lead.

## Zigzagging

Avoid heading straight up or down steep slopes. Climb or descend in zigzags. Use a stick or poles for support when descending.

climbing

descending

## BEAR SAYS

**Crossing frozen terrain is tiring. Take regular breaks to rest, drink water, and maybe eat a trail snack for extra energy. Remember to keep hydrated.**

## Sastrugi

Sastrugi are wind-blown ice ridges. These may cover a large area, all facing in the same direction. Clambering up and down these obstacles is incredibly tiring—it's better to go around them, if possible.

# USING AN ICE AX

Ice axes are climbing aids for snow and ice. They are designed to help mountaineers climb and descend frozen slopes safely. If you start to slide, an ice ax can prevent a serious fall.

### Parts of an ice ax

An ice ax is shaped a bit like a pick. The flattened blade, called an adze, is used to cut steps. Jam the pick into the ice. The shaft also ends in a spike, which can be jammed into the snow.

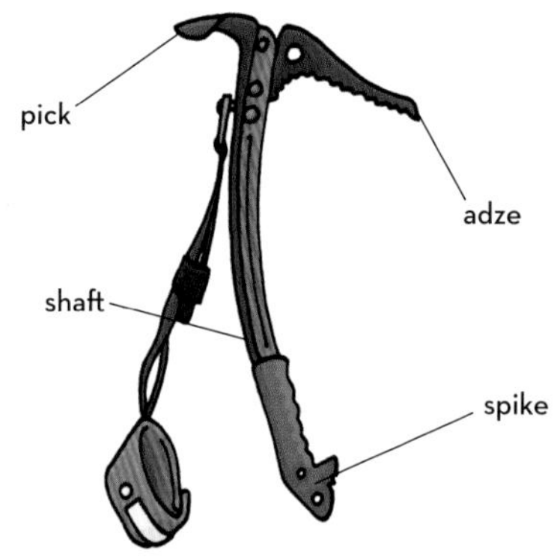

### Carrying an ice ax

Use straps and loops to attach the ice ax to your rucksack for safe carrying. Keep rubber or leather guards on the sharp points when not in use, to avoid injuring yourself or someone else.

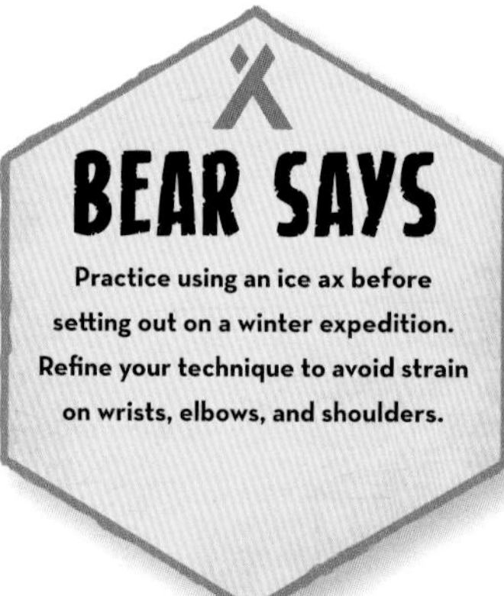

## Cutting steps

Climbers sometimes cut steps to ascend and descend sheer slopes. To do this, swing your ax from the shoulder. Your technique should be smooth and steady. Aim to cut a horizontal step—this may take several blows. Cut one step at a time, move onto the step, then start on the next step.

## Self-belay

Use your ice ax as an anchor when climbing or descending slopes in crampons. Grip the ax head with your upper hand. With each step, drive the spike into the snow at the side. If you start to slip, push down with your upper hand while grasping the shaft with your other hand. Descend facing into the slope.

## Self-arrest

**If you slip down an icy slope, you will have to stay calm and act quickly.**

1. Sliding headfirst down a sheer slope is very scary, but don't panic—you can save yourself with your ice ax.
2. Drive the pick into the ice next to your body and grasp it with both hands.
3. Your body will pivot around the ax as you continue falling, so your feet end up downhill.
4. Throw your weight onto the ax while digging in with your toes to slow, and then halt, your fall.

1

2

3

4

# ICE HAZARDS

Ice is great fun for skating and sliding. In very cold places, frozen rivers and lakes are used as highways. However, thin ice is very dangerous. Falling through could bring risk of death or hypothermia, so you need to take great care.

### How ice forms

Ice forms on ponds, lakes, rivers, and even the sea when temperatures fall below freezing. Only the surface is frozen—ice-cold water lurks beneath.

### Safety first

Beware when approaching ice. Only ice more than 4 inches thick should be strong enough to take your weight. Keep off ice that is any thinner. Use a pole or staff to test if ice is solid. Step on if you are absolutely sure it is rock solid, but keep testing the ice ahead as you proceed.

## BEAR SAYS

**Get out of icy water as quickly as possible. If you are unable to get out, shout for help, keeping as much of your body out of the water as you can.**

### Icebergs

Icebergs are chunks of ice that have broken off glaciers. They are a menace to ships and smaller craft in coastal waters. Remember, the bulk of the ice lies below the surface, so keep well clear in a boat or canoe.

## Self-rescue from ice

If you fall through the ice, brace yourself for the shock of the cold water. Keep your head above water if possible, or kick up to the surface. Kick strongly to the ice edge and use your arms to haul yourself out. Jab the ice with an ice ax or knife if you have one. Once out, roll away to avoid breaking through again, and to shed excess water.

**BEAR SAYS**

**Before attempting to rescue someone, assess the situation, establish the dangers, and consider your ability to help. Is the victim in immediate danger or can they hold on while a rescue team is called? Don't become a victim yourself. All life is valuable.**

## Rescuing someone else from ice

Move cautiously toward a person who has fallen through the ice. At all costs, avoid breaking through yourself. Summon help quickly, or scan the shore for aids such as a rope or life jacket. You may be able to use a scarf, pole, branch, or toboggan to reach the victim and haul them to safety. Treat the patient for hypothermia (see page 58).

# WINTER CAMPING

Winter camping can be a great adventure! It can deepen friendships and allow you to get to know new aspects of nature. Careful preparation and the right gear will help you get the most out of a winter camping trip.

## Camping gear

Tents come in many shapes and sizes —a sturdy structure and tough fabric are needed for winter camping. A warm, four-seasons sleeping bag is a must in cold weather. Down-filled bags are very warm, but don't work well if wet. A thick camping mat, mattress, or camp bed will insulate you from cold ground.

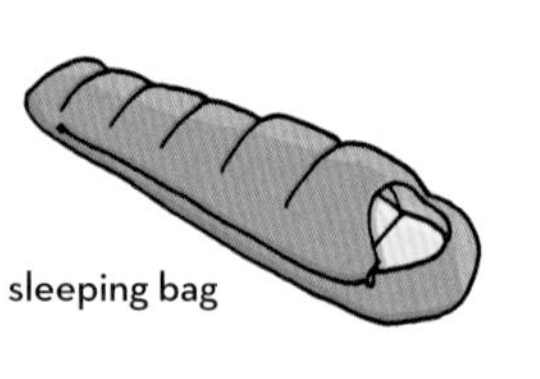

## Cooking kit

Pack food supplies, a stove, matches or a lighter, pans, a mess tin, a mug, and cutlery to prepare hot food.

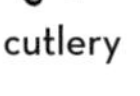

**BEAR SAYS**

**Good hygiene is important for health and comfort, both for yourself and others. Wash yourself and clean your teeth regularly. Be sure to wash your hands before preparing food, and clean kitchen knives and tools.**

## Campsite

Take time to select your campsite. Avoid deep gullies, exposed ridges, and low ground that could flood after heavy rain. Trees and rocky outcrops provide shelter from icy winds.

## Pitching

Pitch your tent in a sheltered spot, making sure to drive in pegs and tighten guy ropes. Site the toilet area away from the tents, washing, and cooking areas, and source snow and ice to melt for water from a different place.

## Camping in a blizzard

Prepare for a blizzard by stringing ropes between tents and the toilet, so you won't get lost in a whiteout. Sit out the storm in your tent. Go outdoors only when you have to, including to clear snow from tents—heavy snow could break poles or rip the fabric. Keep tents well ventilated to allow fresh air to enter.

# SNOW SHELTERS

Snow is a great building material. Because it contains air, it also provides good insulation. Igloos and other snow shelters can help protect you from freezing temperatures and icy winds.

## Build an igloo

**You will need: firm, thick snow, a shovel, a knife.**

1. Cut a number of snow blocks at 15 x 20 x 20 inches. Mark out a circle about 10 ft. in diameter and stamp down the snow.
2. Lay the blocks in a circle. As you complete the bottom layer, shape the blocks with a shovel or knife so they begin to spiral upward.
3. Continue to shape and position blocks spiraling upward and curving in to form a dome. Cut a door and position blocks to form an entrance facing away from the wind.
4. Shape and fit the last block from inside the igloo. Fill any gaps with loose snow.

1

2

3

4

## Square snow shelter

**Building an igloo takes time and skill. A square shelter roofed with a tarpaulin is quicker and easier to build, though not as warm.**

1. Mark a square in the snow the size of your tarp. Cut and lay snow blocks inside the square to form walls about 3 ft. high. Leave a narrow door.
2. Lay a tarp on the walls, crawl inside, and raise the roof with the blunt end of a ski pole. Take care not to pierce the fabric.
3. Anchor the tarp with several smaller blocks of snow. Position larger blocks around the door to make a porch.

1

2

3

**BEAR SAYS**

**Pack down snow to form a sleeping platform in your shelter. Warm air rises, so you will be warmer at a higher level. All shelters need ventilation holes so poisonous waste gases don't build up inside.**

## Quinzhees

Like an igloo, a quinzhee is a traditional snow shelter. It can be made of loose or powdery snow that cannot be shaped into blocks. In a survival situation, a snow hole or pine tree bivouac can also provide some protection from the elements.

### Building a quinzhee

**You will need: snow, a shovel, a rucksack, a tarp, twigs.**

1. Mark a circle in the snow about 8–10 ft. wide. Flatten the snow.
2. Pile your rucksack, gear, and branches in the center to form a rounded heap. Cover with a tarp. The idea is to create a space big enough to curl up in.
3. Shovel 10 inches of snow on top.
4. Gather sticks and measure and mark 10 inches on each. Push the sticks into the dome to check if the walls are thick enough. Add more snow as needed. Leave to harden.
5. Cut an entrance. Tunnel into the dome and carefully remove the rucksack, tarp and other materials. Smooth the inside. Pack down snow to make a sleeping platform. Poke a ventilation hole with a stick or ski pole.

## Making a snow cave

A snowdrift at least 8 ft. deep can be used to make an emergency bivouac. You will need a shovel or ice ax. Dig a tunnel sloping downward into the drift, then upward. Hollow out a sleeping chamber at the end. Use loose snow to make a platform to sit and sleep on. Poke a ventilation hole in the roof.

## Making a fir tree bivouac

In an emergency you can bivouac in the space below a fir tree. Dig out the hollow with a shovel, taking care not to dislodge snow from lower branches. Pack loose snow to form a sleeping platform, and add some leaves and branches to keep you dry.

**BEAR SAYS**

**Work steadily and methodically. If you get hot, remove outer clothing to avoid overheating. Take regular breaks to drink water. Try not to get your clothing soaked.**

# SOURCING WATER

Everyone knows it's important to drink water in hot, dry climates. Yet in cold weather you still need to drink at least 2 liters of water a day to stay healthy. In frozen landscapes, you have to work hard to melt ice and snow to drink.

## Using solar heat

The sun's heat can be used to melt water. Prop a tarp or black plastic bag on sticks, or tie it to a tree. Angle it to face the sun. Heap snow or ice on the plastic, and place a container underneath to catch meltwater. You can also collect water from dripping icicles or thawing streams.

## Melting snow or ice in a pan

Building a fire is the most effective way of melting snow and ice. Bring a little water to a boil in a pan. Add small chunks of ice or snow. Keep adding more as these melt, but make sure the water does not boil away, or the pan will burn.

## BEAR SAYS

**Choose ice over snow for melting. Ice is denser and also melts more quickly. Gather it from unpolluted sources, or filter and boil it to purify.**

## Melting an ice block

A block of ice can be melted on a flat stone that is balanced on large logs on either side of a fire. The stone should slope slightly so meltwater drains into a container.

## Preventing refreezing

Drinking water must be stored carefully to avoid refreezing. Place your water bottle in your sleeping bag at night, but not next to your skin. Water can also be stored under snow. Turn the bottle upside down so if ice does form at the base, you can still drink from the top.

## Snowballs

Pack snow into dense balls. Skewer them on sticks and prop them by a campfire, with containers below to catch the drips. You can also stuff snow into a sock and prop it by the fire.

**BEAR SAYS**

**Don't eat snow or ice, as it will lower your body temperature and put you at risk of hypothermia.**

# WILD WINTER FOODS

In winter, plant foods are scarce, but you may be able to find shoots, roots, and berries left over from fall. Fishing probably offers the best chance of getting a square meal from the wild.

## Berries

Berries provide winter food for birds and animals. Blackberries, salmonberries, and cloudberries can be eaten raw. Bearberries are best cooked. Rose hips are rich in vitamin C—you can stew them to make syrup, jam, or tea.

bearberries

blackberry

salmonberr

cloudberry

rose hips

## Plant foods

The bark and underground shoots of Arctic willow can be eaten raw or cooked. Pine and spruce needles can be boiled for tea. On coasts, many seaweeds are edible. Wash sea lettuce, kelps, and lavers, and boil them until tender.

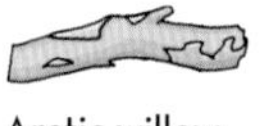
Arctic willow bark

Arctic willow tips

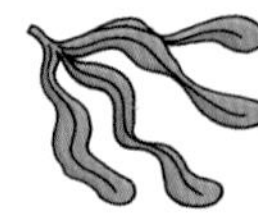
kelp

laver

pine needles

sea lettuce

## Lichen

Lichens are a combination of a plant and a fungus. Species such as reindeer moss and rock tripe can be eaten once cooked.

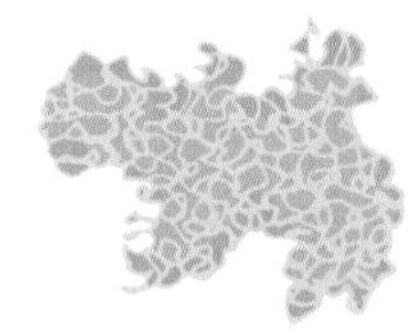
reindeer moss

rock tripe

## Fungi

Some types are edible. Others, such as fly agaric, are deadly poisonous. It's probably best to avoid fungi unless you are an expert.

## Ice fishing

To catch fish swimming under ice, cut a hole in the ice using a saw or a screw called an auger. Drop a baited line into the hole. You can also attach your fishing line to a stout stick and tie a cloth to the other end. Tie on a crosspiece wider than the hole. When a fish bites, the cloth flag will be pulled upright.

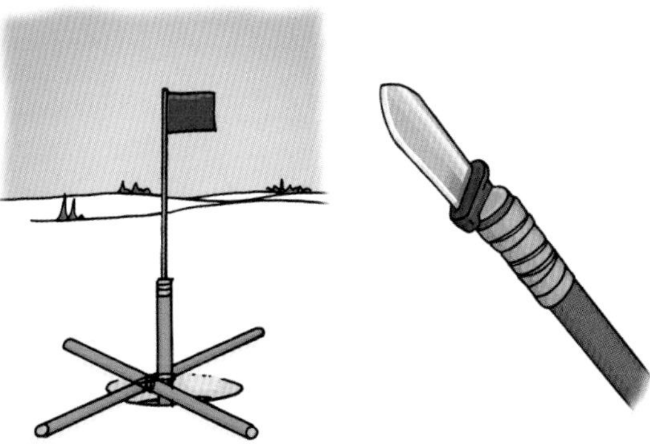

## Preparing fish for cooking

Fish over 2 inches long must be gutted before cooking. Carefully slit the belly with a knife and remove the guts. Fish can be baked in foil, grilled, or spit roasted (see pages 82–83). Cook and eat fish within hours of catching, or it could go bad.

## BEAR SAYS

**You can improvise a fishing spear by binding a knife to a pole, but be sure to bind it very securely. Don't do this if you only have one knife—it's too valuable to risk losing!**

# TRACKING

Winter is a great time to track and observe animals. In a survival situation, you may need to catch animals for food. Meat is a major food for many people skilled in winter survival, such as the Inuit of the Arctic.

## Animal tracks

In winter, animals can be easily identified from the prints they leave in snow, mud, or frost. The prints shown here are from animals that are out and about in winter. A field guide to local wildlife will show more tracks.

## Trails and food remains

Animals leave trails in vegetation as they search for food and patrol their territories. You may also find food remains, such as nibbled nuts.

## Camouflage

Camouflage yourself before going wildlife spotting or hunting. Dress in colors that blend in with the landscape. Stick foliage in your hat or hair. You can use mud to disguise bare skin, such as your hands and face.

## Stalking animals

Check which way the wind is blowing by holding up a wetted finger. Approach animals downwind (with the wind blowing from them to you) or your scent will give you away.

## Using cover

Use the cover of trees and bushes to approach wildlife unseen. Crouch behind rocks or vegetation on a ridge or riverbank, or your silhouette will give you away.

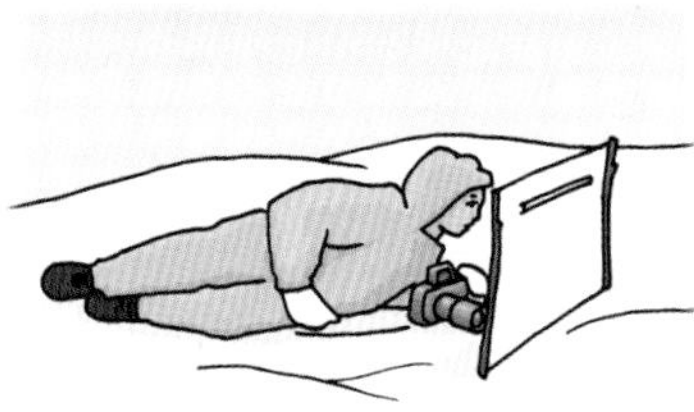

## Making a hunting blind

Arctic hunters use a canvas square called a blind to stalk prey. You can rig a canvas sheet on sticks and cut a narrow slit in the center. Crawl toward the target while hiding behind the blind.

## Setting a snare

Rig a snare by making a running knot in a loop of wire, which will tighten around an animal's neck. Lay the snare on an animal trail, tied to a stake driven into the ground. Position at the head height of prey using twigs.

# FIRE CRAFT

The ability to make fire is especially vital in winter. A campfire will warm and light your camp. You can dry wet clothing and prepare hot food and drink. However, cold, wet, or snowy conditions can make it difficult to get a fire going.

### Gathering materials

Collect all materials needed for a fire. You will need dry tinder to take a spark—gather dry moss, leaves, straw, or bracket fungi. Make sure tinder is bone-dry. You will also need kindling—use dry sticks or split a log with an ax. Finally, you'll need small and then larger logs to fuel the fire.

**It's often said that firewood warms you three times—once when you cut or gather it, once when you split and stack it, and lastly when you light the fire!**

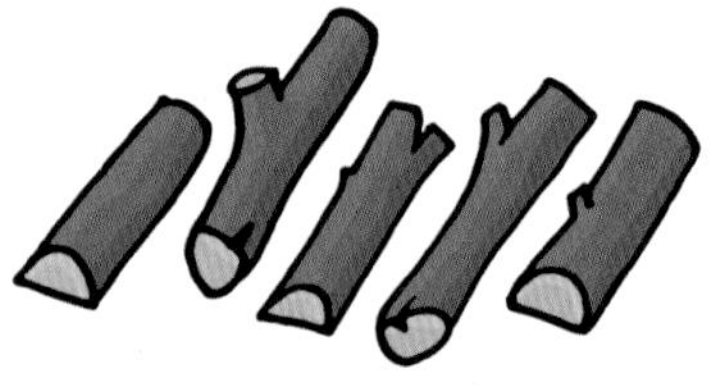

### Fire platform

Lighting a fire on damp or snowy ground is tricky. Build a platform of freshly cut sticks to provide a base for the fire.

### Making a fire screen

A woven screen will shield your fire from the wind and reflect heat to warm you. Drive two pairs of stakes into the ground as shown. Pile sticks into the center to form a wall, and seal any gaps with twigs or moss.

# BEAR SAYS

**Dry wet logs in the sun or by the fire. Cover with a tarp in wet weather. Collect tinder, such as moss, as you travel, and store it in your pockets—your body heat will dry it out.**

## Making fuzz sticks

Fuzz sticks make excellent kindling. Run your knife down a stick to create a long shaving. Try not to detach the shaving. Turn the stick slightly and repeat until the end is covered with shavings.

## Fire lighting

The simplest way to light a fire is by using matches or a lighter. You can also use a fire steel—run the striker along the rod to direct sparks at the tinder. A fire steel won't run out of fuel and will still work when damp.

## Pyramid fire

This kind of fire is easy to light. Build a pyramid of kindling over a ball of tinder. You can also place two large logs on either side of the fire to act as a windbreak, and to form a surface on which to balance cooking pots.

# CAMPFIRE COOKING

In cold weather, you need at least one hot meal a day, and several hot drinks. Hot food and drinks warm you from the inside, and will also raise your spirits. What could be better than a tasty meal cooked on a campfire after a long, cold day outdoors?

## Cooking methods

There are as many ways of cooking food outdoors as there are indoors. Fish, meat, vegetables, and fruit can be baked in foil in the embers of a campfire. You can skewer food on sticks and spit roast it, or grill it on a barbecue. You can fry ingredients in a pan or combine them to make a delicious soup or stew.

## BEAR SAYS

**In wet or snowy conditions, store tools and utensils in a waterproof box, or rolled in a tarpaulin. Don't leave tools lying around where they could get wet or covered with snow.**

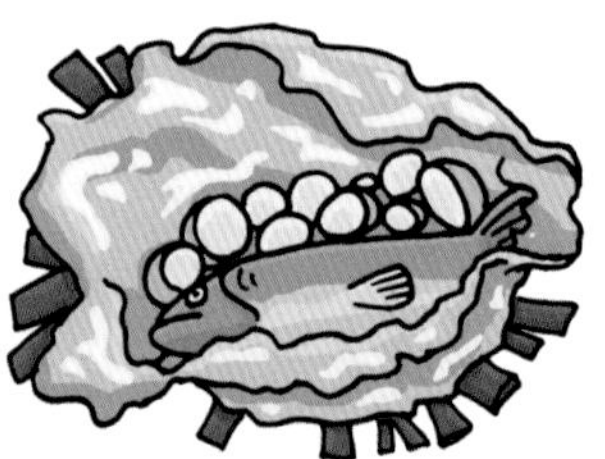

## Making a pot rod

Hang a pot or kettle over a fire using a pot rod. Cut notches in both ends of a long, stout stick. Balance the rod on a forked stick or over a large log. Anchor the end by looping it to a stake driven into the ground, or placing a large stone on top.

## Making tongs

Improvise tongs by lashing together the ends of two stout twigs. Insert a stone or twig between the lashing to keep the prongs open.

## Hot breakfast

Start the day with a hot meal if possible. Heat a pan of warming oatmeal, or cook eggs and bacon in foil in the embers of your fire.

## Kettle tripod

You can also use a tripod to hang a pot or kettle over a campfire. Lash the ends of three stout sticks together, and splay the other ends to form the tripod.

# SKIS AND SNOWSHOES

Traveling on foot over snow is slow and exhausting. Skis and snowshoes offer the chance to cover ground much more quickly—once you've gotten the hang of them. With practice, skiing and snowshoeing are exhilarating, and a lot of fun!

## How they work

Skis and snowshoes work by spreading your body weight over a larger area, which stops you sinking into the snow. Skis allow you to glide over snow and ice at high speed, especially if you're going downhill, which saves energy.

### Cross-country skiing tips

1. Keep your body relaxed with your knees and ankles loose and flexible. Slouch slightly to keep your weight low.
2. Scoot one leg forward at a time. Glide as you shift your weight from ski to ski. Try not to tense or shuffle.
3. Use your ski poles for balance and extra push.
4. As you become more skilled, flex and bounce with each step. In short, kick and glide.

herringbone pattern

snowplow

## Climbing and braking

To climb uphill in skis, plant your feet with toes pointing outward, so your skis make a herringbone pattern in the snow. To descend, brake by pointing the tips of your skis inward—this shape is called a snowplow.

## Snowshoe techniques

To climb uphill in snowshoes, kick with your toes to form flat steps. To move downhill, keep your weight over your feet and plant your feet firmly. Plant your poles in front to keep you steady.

## Making snowshoes

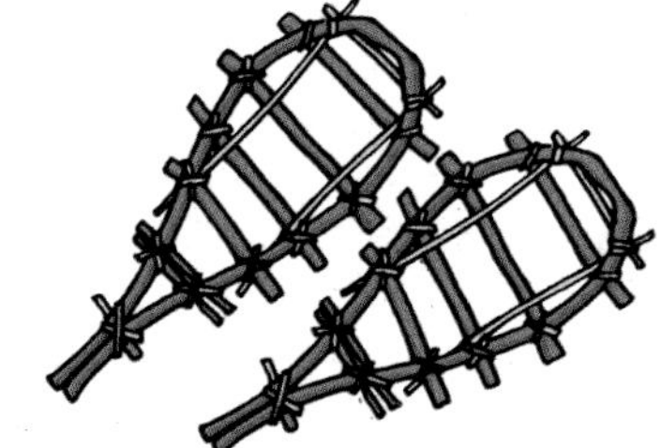

Bend two supple branches into teardrop shapes. Bind cord around the ends. Tie on cross struts and a base for your shoes. You can also use cord to form the base. Loop cord to form a binding to slip your toes in. Your heels should be free so they can lift as you walk.

## Fir branch snowshoes

You can also improvise snowshoes by simply tying a fir branch to each foot. Tie the front tips to your boots so they point upward and don't get stuck in the snow.

# HAULING LOADS AND SLEDDING

As you know, snow and ice are slippery! The lack of traction on frozen surfaces makes it easy to transport heavy gear that would weigh you down if carried on your back, and make the going very tough.

### Using a pulk sled

A pulk, or light toboggan, provides an easy means of hauling heavy weight across snow and ice. Tie on your gear securely. Attach the rope to your waist or a harness. When moving downhill in a group, pair off and position one person at the rear with a rope to act as a brake.

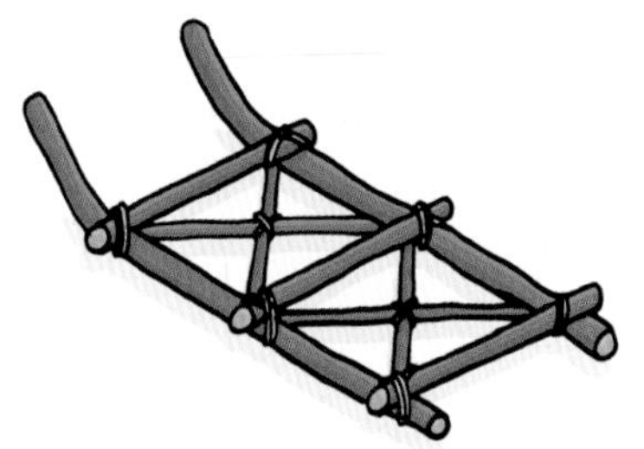

### Improvising a sled

You can make a rough sled using two long, forked sticks for runners. Cut one fork off each stick and smooth with a rasp or knife. The remaining forks will curve upward. Cut notches in the undersides and lash on more poles to form the sled. Attach a rope to the forks.

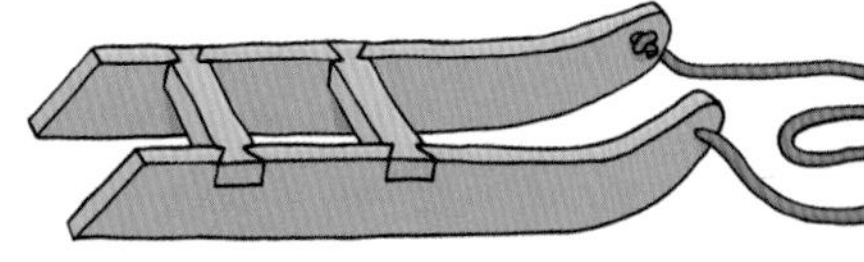

### Making a bobsled

You can also make a simple bobsled by sawing boards, as shown, to form the runners. Use the leftover wood to make the cross struts. Attach a rope to the runners at the front.

## Making a travois

A travois is a frame invented by Native Americans to haul loads. It was traditionally pulled by a horse. Make a travois by lashing the ends of two long poles together. Tie on a couple of cross struts and then lash on your load securely. This device works well on ice or snow.

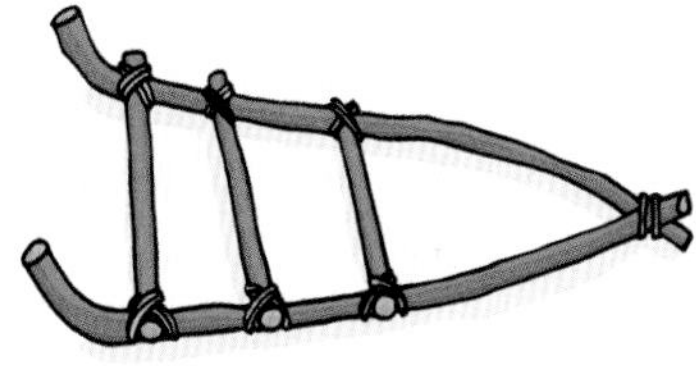

**BEAR SAYS**

**Rubbing wax on the undersides of sled and toboggan runners will make them glide smoothly and go faster.**

## Sledding techniques

Steer a sled with your feet—put your right foot down to turn right, and vice versa. When heading steeply downhill, sit far back with both feet on the ground. Pull up the front to brake. When sledding downhill headfirst, use gloved hands and feet to brake.

# DOG SLEDDNG

For centuries, Arctic peoples have used dogs to pull sleds loaded with their belongings. Nowadays, most people use motorized transportation, but sledding is still a great way to travel over ice and snow.

## Parts of a dog sled

There are many sled designs, depending on the terrain and the amount of gear you need to haul. All dog sleds include skis or runners, traces, or straps connecting dogs to the sled, plus one or more brakes.

brakes
traces
runners
straps
dogs

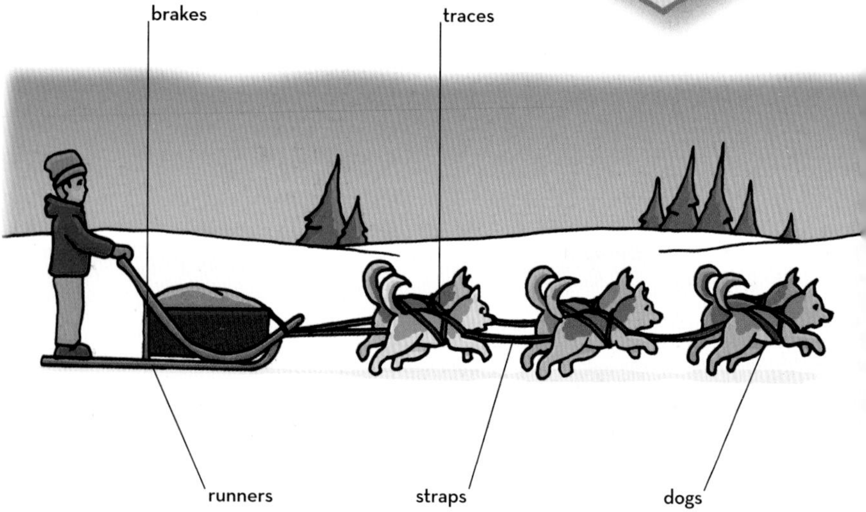

## Formations

Different formations are used to hitch dogs to the sled.

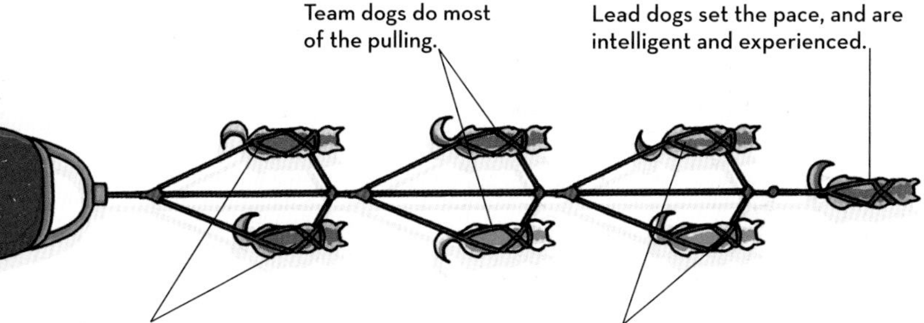


## Tips and techniques

1. When you are ready to set off, ease off the brake and give the command "mush." Get ready for the jerk as the sled starts moving. Experts recommend keeping the brake partly on for a while to control the dogs.
2. Turn right by leaning on your right foot and vice versa. Keep your knees slightly bent to absorb the shock as you hit bumps in the trail.
3. Put the brake on to go downhill. Get off and push to help the dogs when going uphill, but don't let go of the sled! Keep a safe distance behind other sleds, and give the dogs a treat at the end.

# AVALANCHES

An avalanche strikes when a mass of snow and ice breaks loose and thunders down a mountain. These fast and destructive falls are a menace on hills and mountains in winter. Learn to recognize the warning signs, and know what to do in the event of disaster.

## Avalanche types

There are several different types of avalanche, depending on conditions.

### Powder avalanche

Dry, powdery snow cascades downhill at great speed, blasting air before it.

### Slab avalanche

A whole slab of snow breaks loose and slides over a layer of ice crystals.

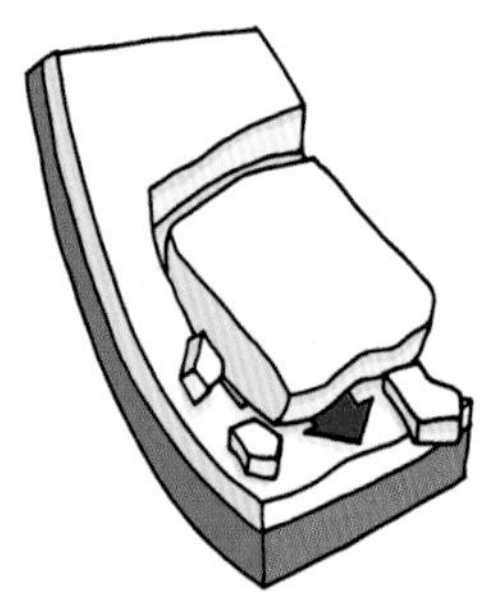

### Wet snow avalanche

Fresh, wet snow sets as hard as concrete when it stops.

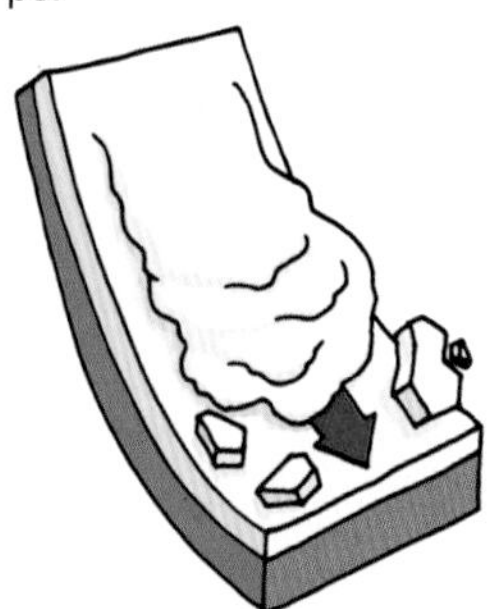

**BEAR SAYS**

**Beware of steep slopes where deep drifts have formed, and snow-choked gullies. The danger increases as sun warms the snow, so set off early to cross danger zones. Pack a shovel, probe, and beacon in areas prone to avalanches.**

## Causes

Avalanches may be set off by rising temperatures, loud noises, and even vibrations from a passing skier. Experts sometimes trigger avalanches through controlled explosions. An avalanche can roar downhill at up to 220 mph, destroying forests, roads, bridges, and buildings in its path.

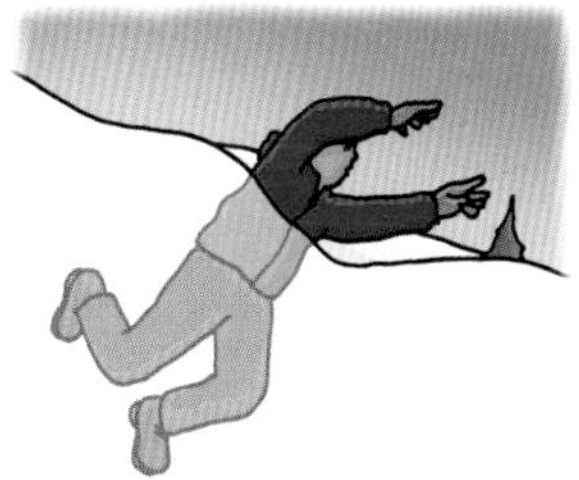

## What to do in an avalanche

**The best thing to do is avoid any area where there is an avalanche risk, but if you do get caught in an avalanche there are several things you can do.**

1. If you feel an avalanche start, you may be able to race uphill or to the side to escape it. If you can't, take shelter behind a rock outcrop or sturdy tree. Ditch your gear.
2. If caught in an avalanche, use a swimming motion to stay at the surface. Try to reach the edge. Clamp a hand over your nose and mouth to avoid swallowing snow.
3. As the avalanche stops, you have just a short time before it sets hard. Clear a breathing space in front of your face, to provide precious minutes of air.
4. Spit to find which way is up. Try to kick or claw your way to the surface, or at least get a hand out. If you can't reach the surface, can you activate your mobile phone or rescue beacon? If you hear rescue coming, shout to show your position.

# GLACIERS

Glaciers are huge masses of ice that flow very slowly downhill. Like avalanches, they can menace winter expeditions. However, with the right gear and expert guidance, climbers can cross glaciers safely.

## How do glaciers form?

Glaciers form in bowl-shaped hollows called cirques, high in mountains. The snow builds up and packs down to form ice. Eventually the weight of the ice sets the glacier moving. As it flows downhill, ice breaks off at the tip and crashes down below.

## Parts of a glacier

Deep, vertical cracks called crevasses form where the ice splits and splinters. Debris called moraine is carried at the sides, on top, and at the tip, or snout. A stream of meltwater trickles from the snout. Glaciers bulldoze deep, U-shaped valleys as they flow downhill.

## Beware crevasses

Crevasses may be hidden by fresh snow. Snow bridges sometimes form over these cracks—they may or may not be strong enough to take your weight. The leader should proceed very cautiously, while the others pay out the rope, ready to take the strain if the leader falls.

## Techniques

1. Rope up for safety. All teams should have an experienced leader. The leader may use a probe to check if the ice ahead is stable.
2. Crevasses usually extend farther than you can see at the surface. Detour around them if possible.
3. A diagonal formation is a safe way to cross a crevasse field.

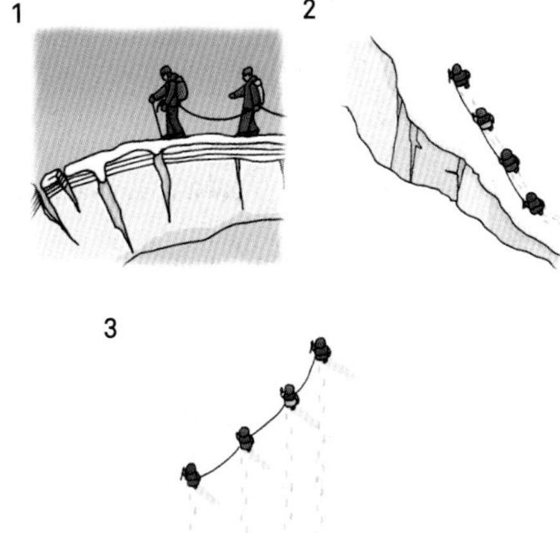


## BEAR SAYS

**To explore a glacier, you need full climbing gear, including a helmet, harness, crampons, ice ax, and rope. Prepare by practicing ice climbing moves. Read up on hazards.**

## Rescue from a crevasse

If a climber falls into a crevasse, the rest of the team self-arrest using ice axes (see pages 64–65). The climber may be able to climb out unaided. If not, the team must haul them to safety, often using a pulley.

# WINTER EMERGENCIES

Winter is a great time to be outdoors. This section has explored the hazards of extreme cold, snow, and ice, and the skills you need to survive them. However, accidents can still happen. The tips here explain what to do in an emergency.

### Emergency drill

If disaster strikes, the top priority is to get yourself to safety. Rescue others if you can safely do so. Can you raise the alarm using your phone? Be ready to explain where you are. Keep calm and assess the situation. Is anyone injured? Is everyone out of danger? What resources are at hand?

### Stay or go?

If you are lost or stranded, will someone raise the alarm and send rescue? If so, you should probably stay where you are. Try to build a shelter and light a fire. If no one knows you are missing, you may need to seek help. On the trail, take regular breaks and keep hydrated. Watch for signs of exposure, and avoid sitting or lying on wet or snowy ground.

### Emergency signals

There are two main types of signals: visual (sight) and audio (sound) signals. Visual signals include flags, flares, fire, smoke, and light flashes. Audio signals include shouts and whistle blasts.

## Visual signals

Bright colors and straight lines stand out well against snow. You could use rocks or branches to write an SOS message in the snow.

## SOS

The letters SOS are an international distress call. The Morse code for SOS is three short signals (dots), three long ones (dashes), and another three short ones. Three of any signal is also a distress call—such as three light flashes or three whistle blasts.

## Ground-to-air signals

Ground-to-air signals also stand out well against snow. If rescue comes by air, you may need to find a landing spot. Search for flat, open ground. Remove stones and mark with flags. Stand clear if a helicopter or plane prepares to land.

pick us up

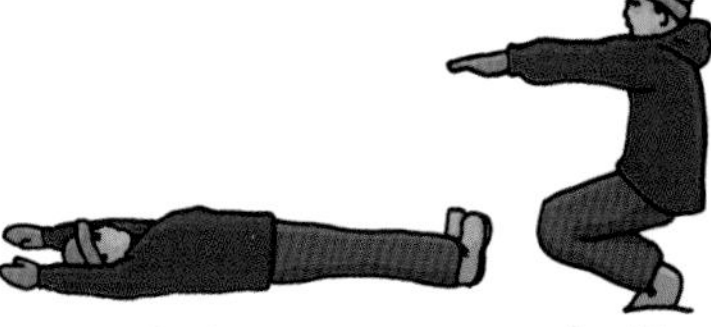

medical assistance needed

land here

## In a snowbound vehicle

Prepare for winter car journeys by packing drinking water, a hot drink in a thermos, snacks, a shovel, and a blanket. If you get stuck in a snowdrift, take any gear out of the trunk immediately. Keep a window open slightly to let in air, and run the engine as little as possible. Sit tight until help arrives!

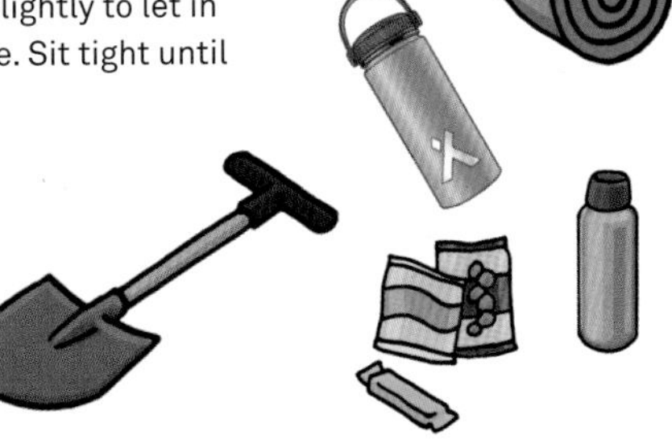

# SUMMER

In summer, the weather is mostly warm and dry, shrubs and trees will be in bloom, and there will be lots of plants and animals for you to discover. This section will give you all the skills you need to make the most of a summer adventure—so get out there and have fun!

Bear

# IN THIS SECTION:

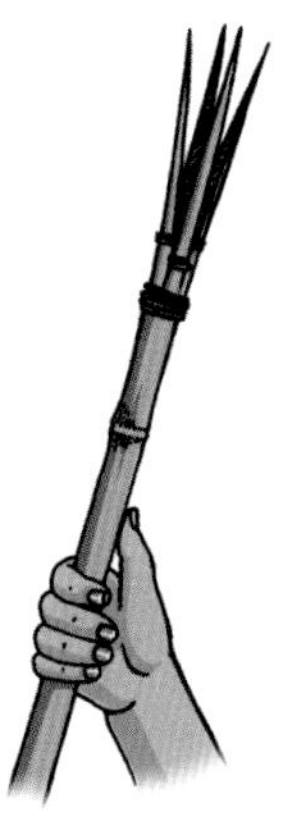

# GEAR AND CLOTHING

Summer is a great time to get outdoors, whether you go hiking, camping, swimming, boating, or just for a walk around your local area. However, you need to hone your survival skills to stay safe in the wild. Preparation is vital—and that includes taking the right gear.

## Clothing

In summer, it's best to wear cotton or a fabric that absorbs sweat. Pack a warm layer in case it gets cool, and always bring wet-weather gear, as you never know when you might get caught in a summer downpour! You'll need sturdy, waterproof boots and a sun hat. Convertible pants can transform into shorts. Avoid tight jeans, as they'll restrict your movement and get soaked through if it rains.

## Sun protection

The sun's rays are fiercest in summer. Exposed skin can burn in just a few minutes, so cover up or apply sunscreen or sunblock. Wear sunglasses to protect your eyes from sunlight, and never look directly at the sun. Drink plenty of water, as dehydration is a risk in summer heat.

## Equipment

These items are important for all summer expeditions.

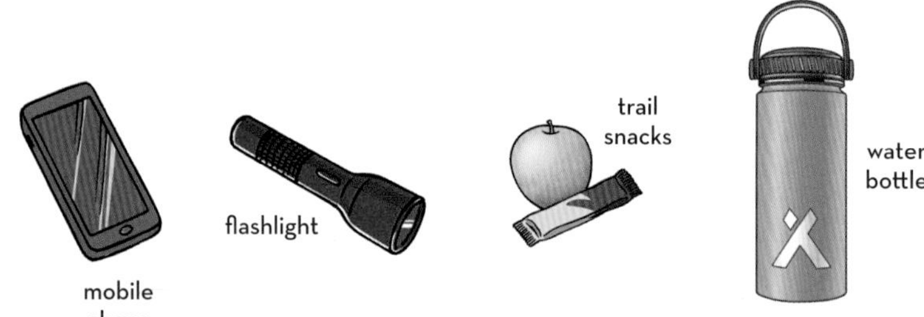

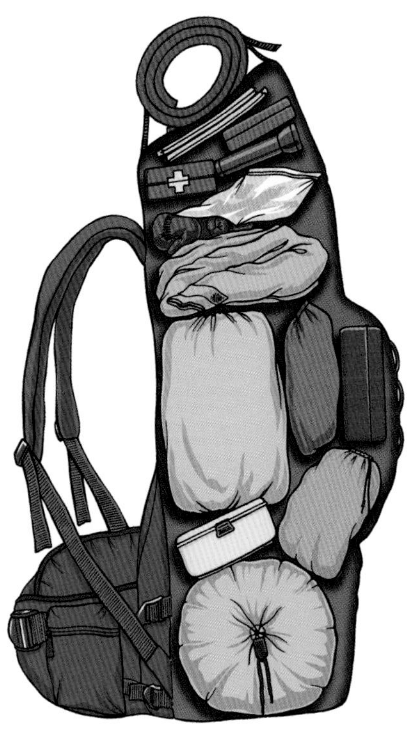

## Packing your rucksack

Knowing how to correctly pack your rucksack can save you a lot of time and energy. Pack your rucksack in reverse order, with the things you need first on top, and items, such as your sleeping bag, that you won't need until you reach camp, at the bottom. Put essential gear, such as your map and water bottle, in side pockets where you can get to them easily. If there is a chance of rain, pack your things in plastic bags to keep them dry. Some rucksacks come with a built-in waterproof liner.

**BEAR SAYS**

**Your rucksack should have a hip belt to take the weight off your shoulders. Adjust straps for maximum comfort.**

# WEATHER WATCHING

Summer weather is generally pleasant, but be careful because it can be changeable. A clear blue sky can quickly turn cloudy, bringing with it a risk of rain and thunderstorms. Stay alert for hazards such as wind, mist, and fog.

## How thunderstorms form

In hot, sticky weather, warm, moist air rises to form tall, dark cumulonimbus clouds. The tops of these clouds develop a positive electric charge (shown on the diagram as a red +), while the base becomes negatively charged (shown as a blue –). When the charge is great enough, lightning sparks between clouds, or from clouds to the ground.

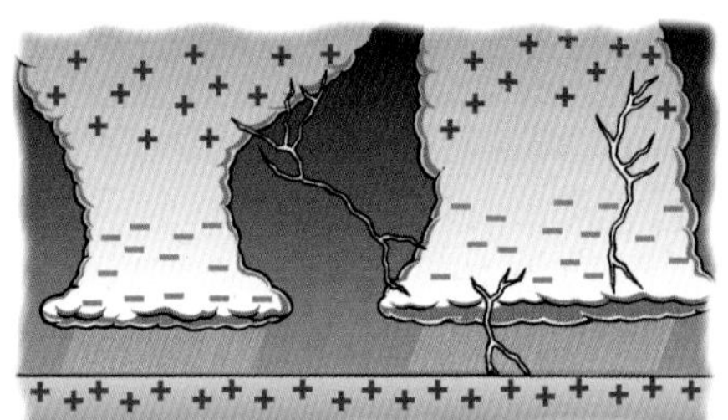

## Sheltering in a storm

Don't shelter on an exposed ridge or under a lone tree, as these places can attract lightning. If you're swimming, leave the water immediately. You'll be safer in a car, valley, wood, or in a ditch or gully. If possible, try to get indoors. If caught in the open, discard metal objects such as walking poles and umbrellas. Crouch down and raise your arms to protect your head.

## How far away?

You can work out how far away a storm is by counting the seconds between the lightning flash and thunderclap. Sound takes five seconds to travel a mile, so divide the number of seconds by five.

## Mountain weather

Mountains have a much colder climate than lowland areas, even in summer. The weather up there changes fast, and can get worse in just a few minutes. Prepare for cold, windy conditions on summits and wear several layers of clothing.

## Mist and fog

These hazards are caused by low-level cloud. In thick fog, it's very hard to get your bearings. You will need a map and compass to find your way (see pages 106–109).

**Always check the forecast before setting out on an expedition. Be aware of changing conditions, such as gathering clouds and rising winds.**

## Weather maps

Knowing how to read weather maps will be invaluable on a summer expedition, with the risk of fast-changing weather. These maps use symbols to show sunshine, clouds, rain, and also wind speeds and direction. Lines called isobars link places with the same air pressure. When isobars are close together, it will likely be wet and windy.

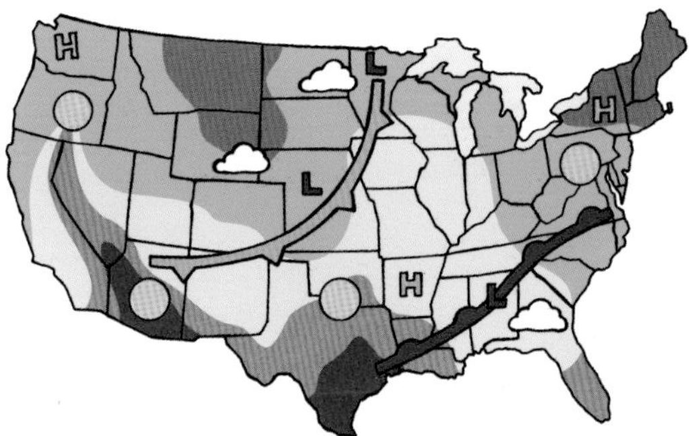

# HOT WEATHER HEALTH

You need to be careful in hot weather, as there are several risks to your health. The body's natural cooling system can fail, bringing about heatstroke, and direct sunlight can badly burn unprotected skin. Take action to avoid these nasty effects of summer weather.

## Heat exhaustion

Heat exhaustion is caused by excessive sweating in hot, humid conditions. The skin feels clammy, and you may feel weak, dizzy, or even delirious. If you feel this coming on, rest in the shade and drink water with a pinch of salt to replace lost fluids.

## Heatstroke

Also called sunstroke, this is the most serious form of heat exhaustion and can be fatal if left untreated. Symptoms include high temperature, fast pulse, headaches, dizziness, nausea, and vomiting. Rest in the shade under a damp sheet or with a fan to cool down, and drink cool water or juice.

## Sunburn

A bad sunburn can blister the skin and, in extreme cases, lead to skin cancer. Prevent sunburn by covering your skin or applying sunscreen. To treat sunburn, protect against sunlight and apply calamine lotion, or cool the skin with a damp cloth.

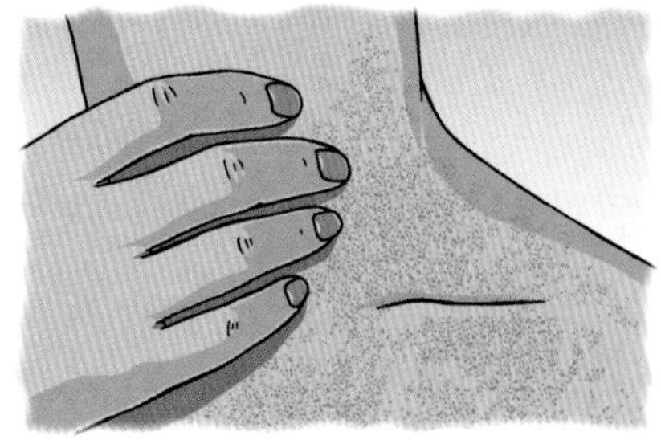

## Prickly heat

This uncomfortable skin irritation can happen when excessive sweating blocks sweat pores. Remove any clothing, wash the affected skin in cool water, and put on dry clothes.

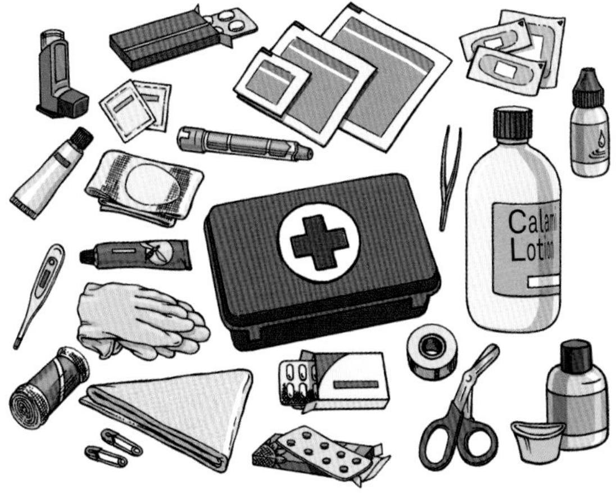

## First aid kit

For any expedition, make sure you pack a first aid kit including painkillers, bandages, medical tape, scissors, bite and sting cream, insect repellent, tweezers, latex gloves, and any medication that specific expedition members may need, such as EpiPens or asthma inhalers.

## Sterilizing wounds

Infection can set in fast in hot weather. Be sure to sterilize any wounds by washing carefully and applying antiseptic.

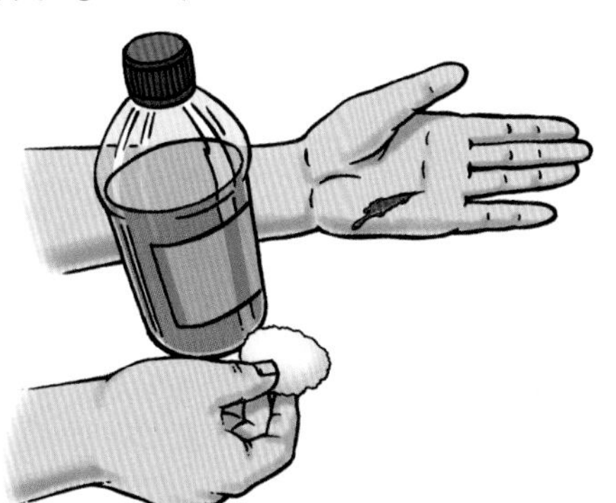

# SUMMER HIKING

Summer is one of the best seasons to go hiking. Long hours of daylight allow for lengthy walks, but beware the sun around midday. The tips on this page will help you get the most out of a hiking trip.

## Hiking gear

Don't forget these important items of gear on a hiking trip.

compass

sun hat

waterproof jacket

hiking boots

healthy, high-energy snacks

warm soc

emergency blanket

warm layers

## Footwear

A sturdy pair of walking boots is invaluable on any hike. In dry conditions, walking shoes will also work well and are slightly cooler than boots.

## Blisters

When it comes to blisters, prevention is better than a cure. Smear petroleum jelly between the toes to prevent rubbing. Take action as soon as you notice soreness. Remove boots and socks and apply a bandage or moleskin to protect the sore spot. If you do get a blister, don't pop it, or you will risk infection.

### Walking stick

A good walking pole will provide extra stability. You can also use it to test the depth of streams or marshes, and keep brambles, nettles, and any curious animals at bay.

**Tell someone where you are going and what time you expect to reach your destination, so they can raise the alarm if you don't appear.**

### Climbing and descending

It's better to climb slowly and steadily rather than rushing and then having to stop to catch your breath. Zigzag up and down steep slopes. Tighten your boots before descending. Keep your knees bent and use your stick to take your weight.

### River crossings

Scout along the bank for the best place to cross, such as a shallow place or stepping stones. Undo the waist strap of your rucksack. Use your stick for stability. If in a group, link arms or hold on to rucksack straps.

# NAVIGATION

Knowing how to read a map is vital both for short hikes and major expeditions. You should also carry a compass and know how to use it. With a map and a compass, you can find your way anytime, anywhere!

## Map symbols

Maps are drawings of the landscape from above. Features such as water, trees, tracks, and buildings are shown using symbols. The key, or legend, at the side explains what the symbols mean. On most maps, north is at the top.

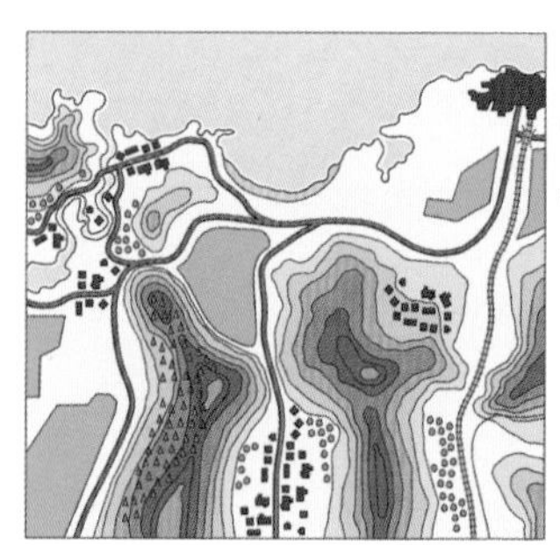


## Contour lines

Contour lines show hills and valleys on the flat surface of a map. These lines link places at the same height above sea level. The height is also given in small figures. Check the figures to see if the land slopes up or down. Allow more time to climb steep hills.

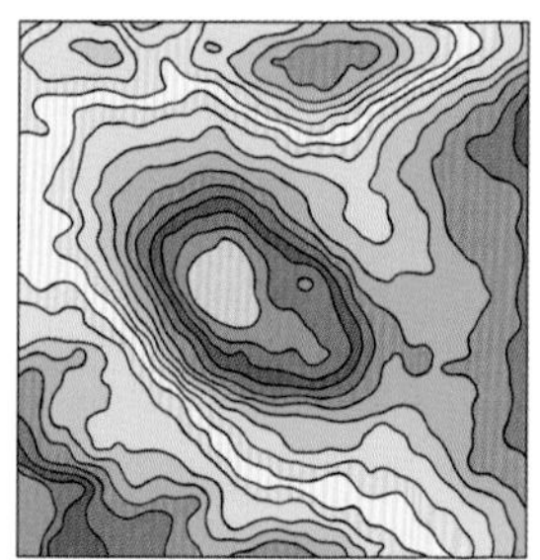

## Grid references

Most maps are divided into a grid of squares. Each square is numbered, which allows you to find locations. Grid references give the east-west position first, then the north-south position. Counting the grid lines crossed on your route provides a rough idea of distance.

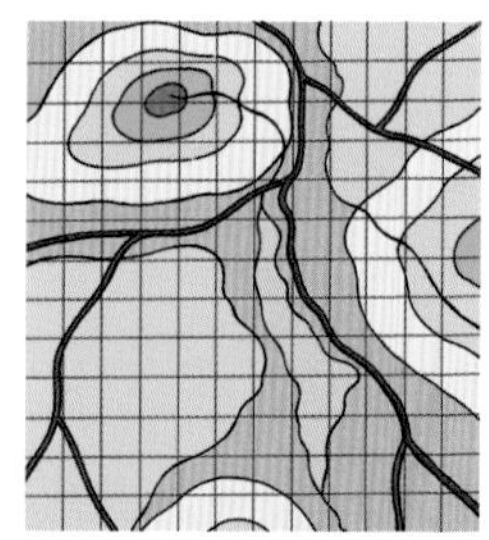

## Scale

Everything on a map is drawn to the same size, called the scale. The scale bar in the key will help you to estimate how long a journey will take.

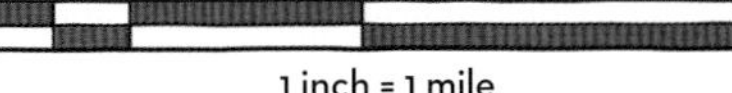

1 inch = 1 mile

## Compass

The red magnetic needle on a compass always points north. Hold the compass flat so the needle rotates freely, and keep it away from any metal objects, which could distort the reading.

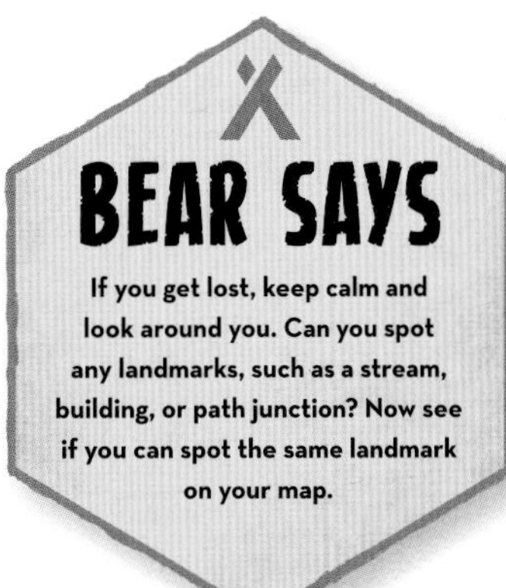


## Using a map and compass

1. Rotate the inner dial so the red arrow points north on the map. The lines on the dial lie over the gridlines on the map.
2. Turn your body so the red magnetic arrow hovers over the red arrow. Now the features you see around you will relate to what's shown on the map.

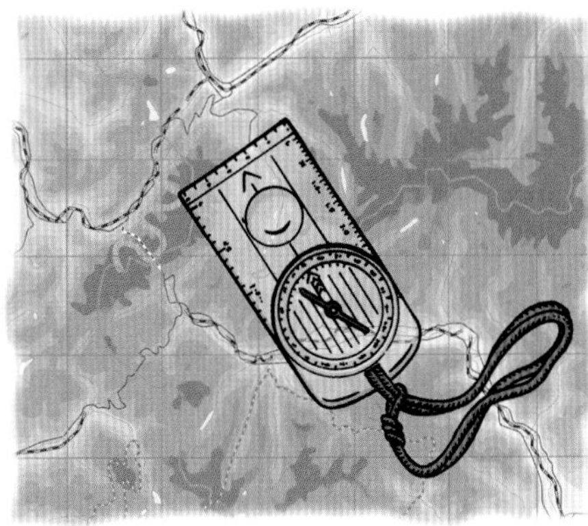

## Navigating without a compass

A compass is the easiest way to navigate in the wild. It allows you to get your bearings, so you know which way to head. However, it is still possible to work out your direction if you don't have a compass.

### Using a sun stick

**Use this method on a sunny day to find the four main compass points: north, south, east, and west.**

1. Push a long, straight stick into the ground. Mark the tip of the stick's shadow with a stone or twig.
2. Wait at least 15 minutes—an hour or more, if possible. The shadow will have moved around. Mark the new position with a second marker.
3. Draw a line between the two markers. This is your east-west line. Draw a second line at right angles to the first—this is your north-south line.

1

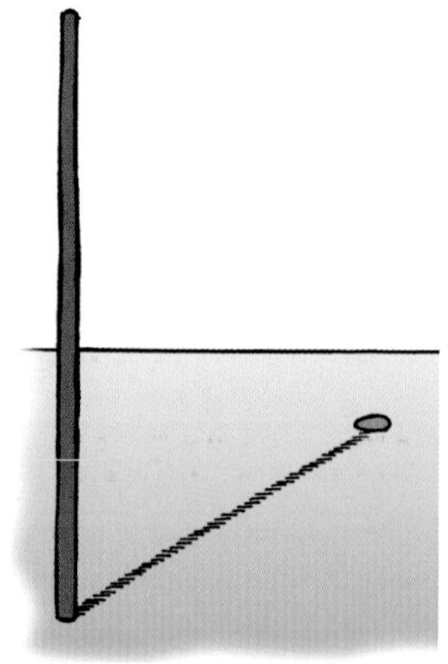

2

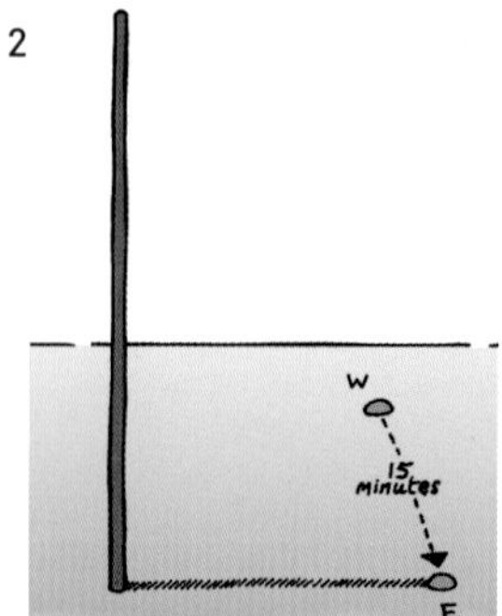


3

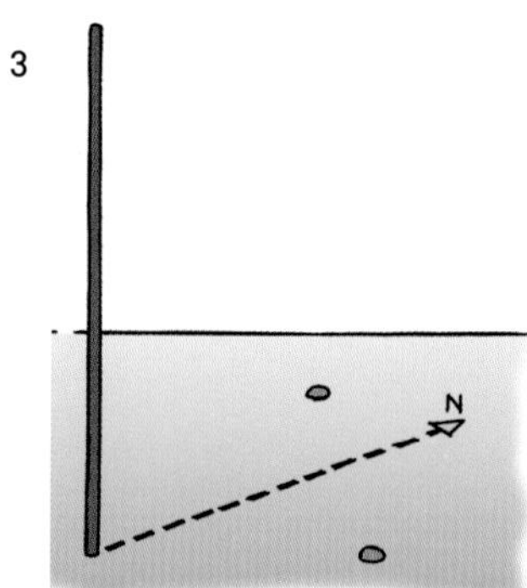

## Using a wristwatch

This method is different in the northern and southern hemispheres. Hold your watch flat. In the northern hemisphere, point the hour hand at the sun. A line midway between the hour and 12 o'clock on your watch points due south. In the southern hemisphere, point 12 o'clock on your watch at the sun. A line midway between this and the hour hand points due north.

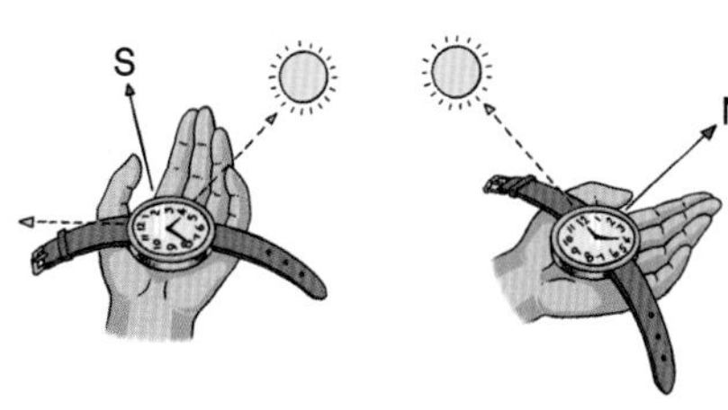


## Navigating by the stars

In the northern hemisphere, the tip of the Big Dipper points to the bright North Star, due north. In the southern hemisphere, the base of the Southern Cross (near a dark, starless patch called the Coal Sack) points south.

the Big Dipper

the Southern Cross

## Making a DIY compass

Improvise a compass using a needle and a small bar magnet. Stroke the magnet along the length of the needle in one direction. Repeat many times. Place the magnetized needle on a leaf, piece of bark or paper, and float in water. It will settle to point north-south. Use the general direction of the sun to work out which is north.

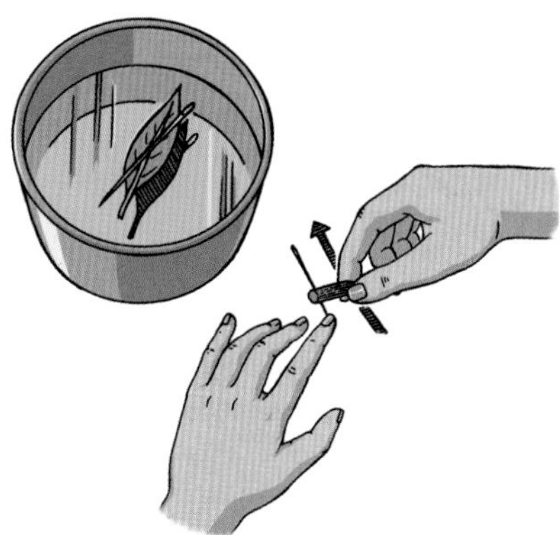

# SIGNS AND SIGNALS

Signaling is an important skill. It allows you to communicate with others, mark a trail, and raise the alarm in an emergency. Summer is a great time to practice signaling, as it is likely to be sunny and dry. You will need basic equipment: a flashlight, a whistle, and a small mirror.

## Types of signal

There are two main types of signals—visual (sight) and audio (sound). These relate to our main senses, sight and hearing.

## Trail signs

Scouts invented trail signs to mark the route for others to follow. You can use sticks, stones, or even tufts of grass to mark a trail.

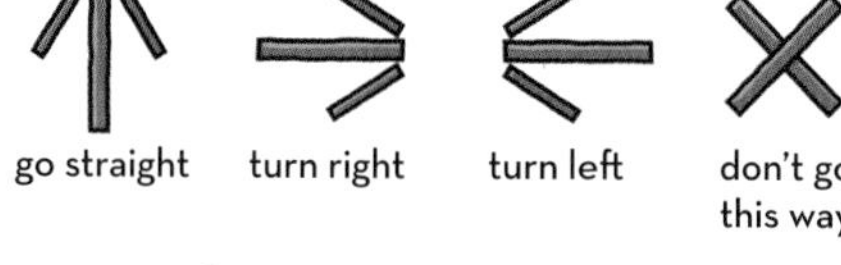


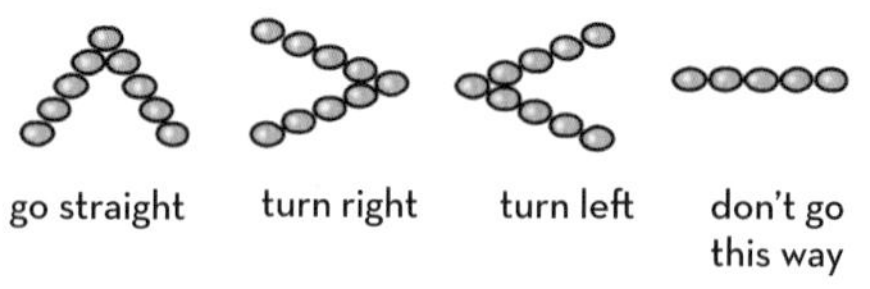


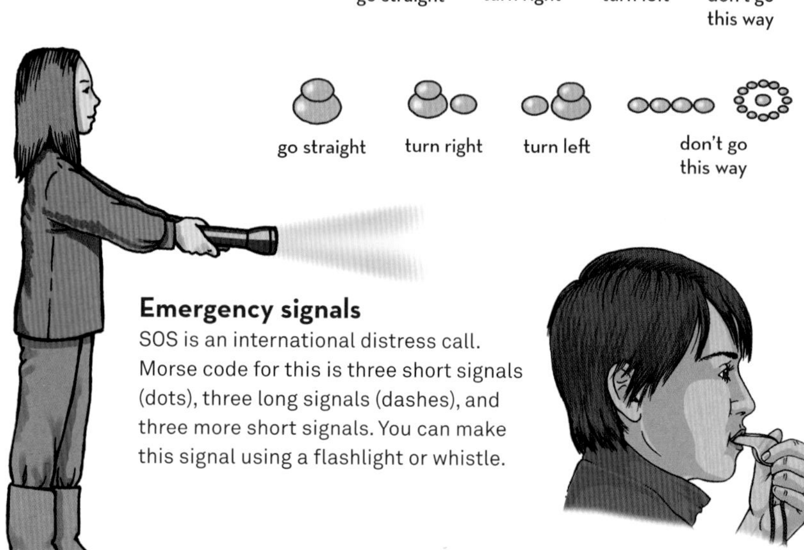


## Emergency signals

SOS is an international distress call. Morse code for this is three short signals (dots), three long signals (dashes), and three more short signals. You can make this signal using a flashlight or whistle.

## Signaling with a mirror

A flash of light from a mirror can be seen from far away. You can signal to your group or to an aircraft in an emergency. Hold the mirror at shoulder height and point toward the sun. Stretch out your other arm and spread your fingers. Now angle the mirror so reflected light passes between your fingers onto the target.

## Body signals

Body signals can be used to communicate with aircraft in an emergency. Position yourself in the open and give signals very clearly.

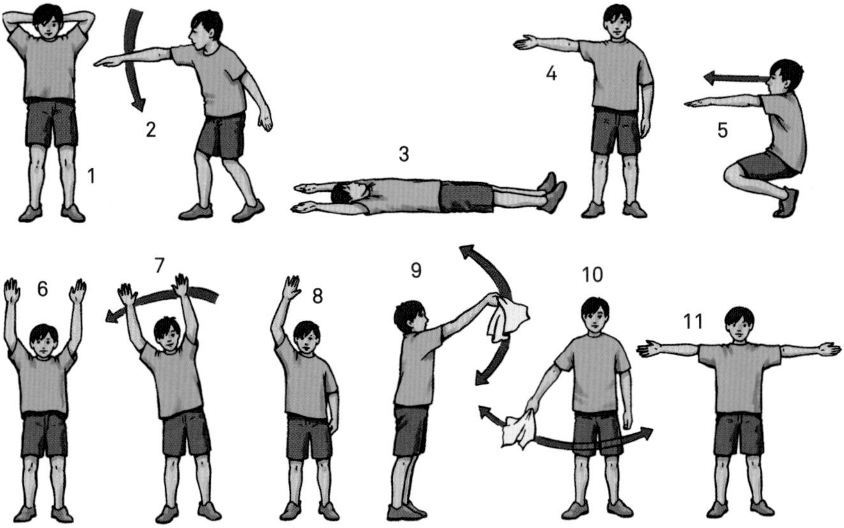

### Key

1. Our receiver is operating
2. Use drop message
3. Need medical assistance
4. Wait, I can proceed shortly
5. Land here
6. Pick us up
7. Do not attempt to land here
8. All OK, do not wait
9. Yes
10. No
11. Need mechanical help

# SUMMER CAMPING

Warm weather and light evenings make summer the best time for camping. The right gear will help you stay warm and comfortable overnight in the wild.

## Choosing a tent

Tents come in different shapes and sizes. Practice putting up and taking down a new tent before a camping trip.

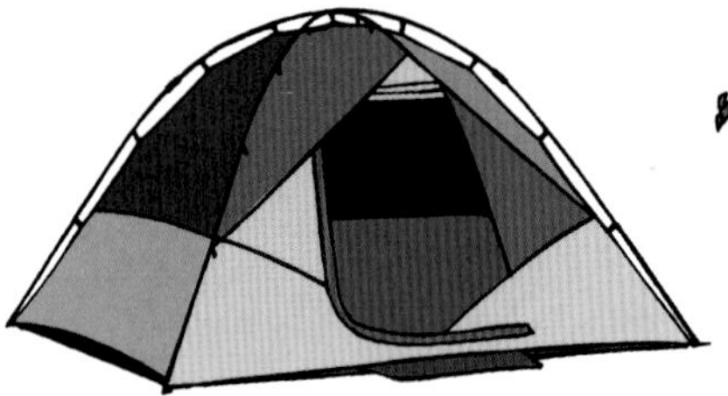

## Sleeping bags

These are generally graded by season—in most places, you will only need a light bag for summer. Bags filled with man-made fiber are relatively cheap and effective, even if wet. You can also buy down-filled bags, but these are very warm and are ineffective when wet, so are most likely inappropriate for summer camping.

## Mattresses

Camping mats and mattresses provide comfort and insulation from damp ground. A foam mat is light to carry. In a survival situation, you could make a bough bed (see page 117).

## Camping gear

These items will come in handy when camping.

portable shower

## Cooking gear

You'll need pots, pans, and other utensils if you intend to cook in the wild.

drinking water

cutting board

camping mug

cutlery

dish towel

pan

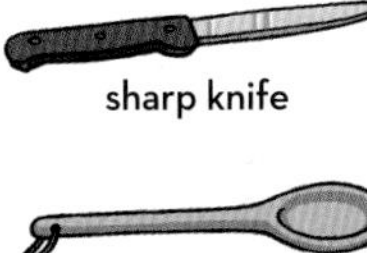


## Stoves

Camping stoves provide instant heat that is easy to control. Various designs run on gas or solid fuel. Don't forget to take spare fuel. You can also cook on a campfire or with charcoal on a barbecue.

**BEAR SAYS**

**Plan camp menus in advance, and make a list of all the ingredients you need. You don't want to start cooking only to discover that a vital ingredient is missing!**

## Making camp

Your camp is a home away from home. It's a place to sleep, eat, bond with friends, and get close to nature. The right location and good organization will help your camp run more efficiently.

## Campsite location

Site your camp near a source of wood and water. Don't get too close to water though, or you risk being flooded or eaten by mosquitoes! The best sites are sheltered yet sunny. Beware rotten trees or branches that could fall and hurt you or damage your equipment. Also beware ant, wasp, and bee nests.

**BEAR SAYS**

**Don't leave tools and gear lying around, as they could get wet or rusty. Choose a place to keep equipment, and ask everyone to return things after use.**

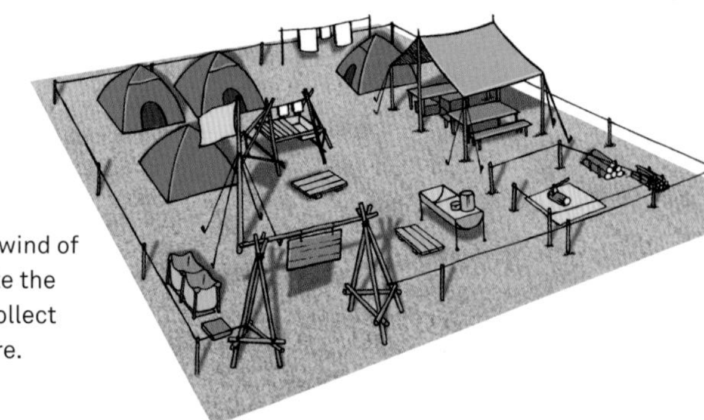

## Camp layout

Build your campfire downwind of tents so sparks can't ignite the fabric. Select a place to collect water and don't wash there.

## Pitching tents

Choose flattish ground and remove debris. Hammer pegs in firmly, trying not to bend them. Pull guy ropes taut to keep the tent from being blown down if it gets windy.

## Timber hitch

This is a good knot for attaching cords to posts or saplings. Loop one end around the post and then over the standing cord. Thread the end below the cord over the post several times. Tighten by pulling the standing cord.

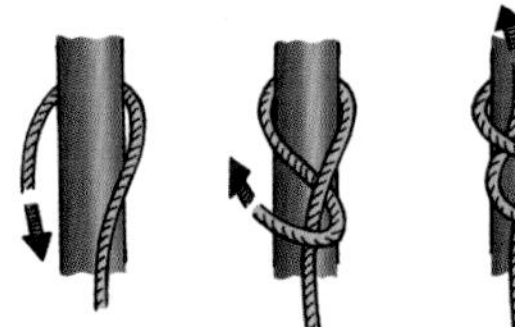

## Food cache

Keep food in tightly sealed containers. In bear country, you will need to cache food high in the air. Tie the bag to a rope, throw the rope over a high branch and hoist into the air.

## Ticks and insects

Mosquitoes can carry dangerous diseases. Apply jungle-strength repellent and keep your skin covered. Sleep under a mosquito net. Beware ticks in woods and on farmland. If one gets stuck in your skin, use tweezers to seize the body, wait a split second, then pull gently, so the head comes out too.

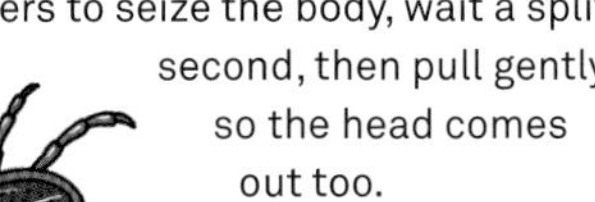

tick

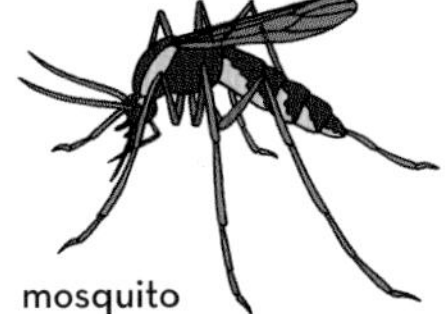

mosquito

# EMERGENCY SHELTERS

A shelter protects you from the elements. It helps you to get a good night's sleep, so you can be alert the next day. Summer is a great time to practice building shelters with rope and tarpaulin, or just using natural materials around you.

## Tarp shelters

With rope and a tarp or plastic sheet, you can quickly rig a basic shelter to keep the rain off. There are several different designs. Make sure the entrance to your shelter faces away from the wind.

### Triangular shelter

Lash two stout, forked sticks together to form an A-shape and drive into the ground. Attach a guy rope or ridgepole sloping backward. Throw a tarp over and secure the edges with stones or pegs. Fold any excess material inside.

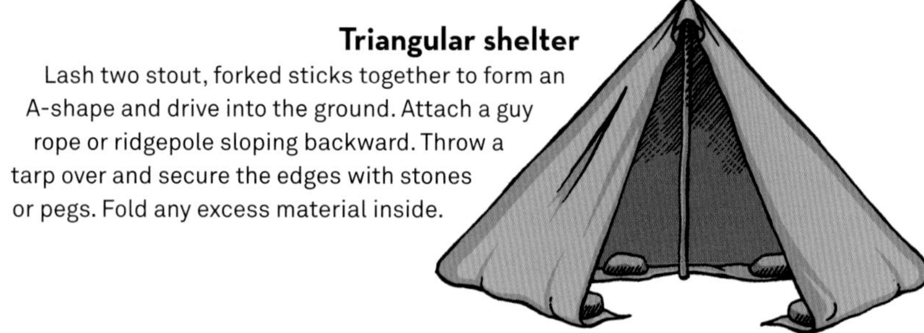

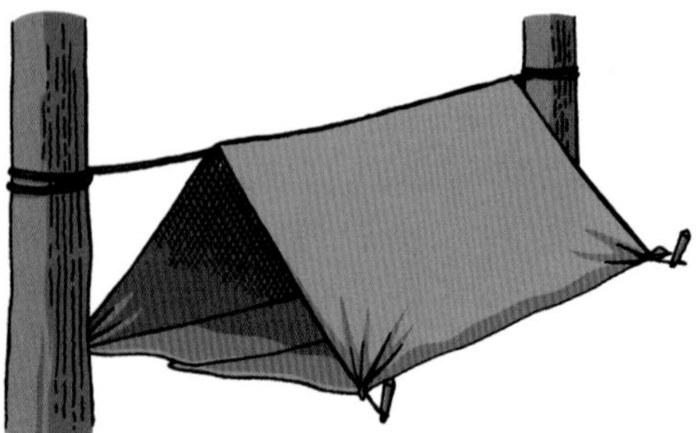

### Fold-over shelter

Drive two stout branches into the ground. Secure with guy ropes if needed. Tie a cord between the uprights and pull taut. Throw a tarp over, attach cords, and peg it down. Fold the excess material under to make a groundsheet.

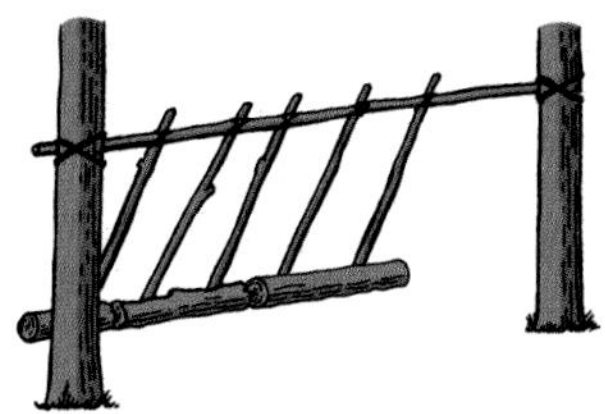

## Building a forest lean-to

1. Lash a long, straightish branch between two uprights at around waist height to form a ridgepole. Peg logs to form the base of the shelter.
2. Lash 4–5 straightish branches sloping from the ridgepole to the base. Weave lots of smaller, supple, leafy branches between these to form a roof. Start at the bottom and work up.
3. If desired, drive shorter branches into the ground at the sides, and weave in twigs to form walls.

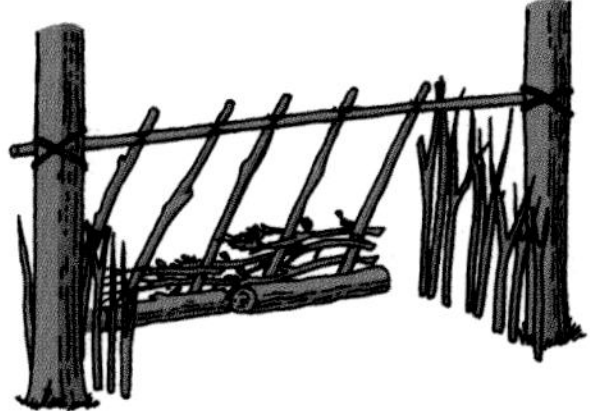

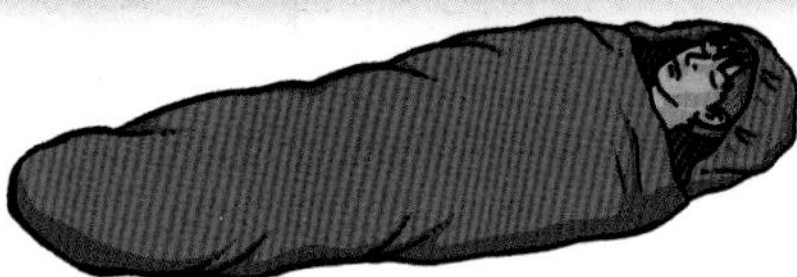

## Bivouac in the open

A bivy bag is a large, waterproof bag that provides emergency shelter. You may be able to pile rocks to form walls for a windbreak.

## Making a bough bed

Dry leaves, bracken, and grass can be used as bedding. You can also pile spruce or pine branches inside a bed-shaped frame of branches pegged to the ground.

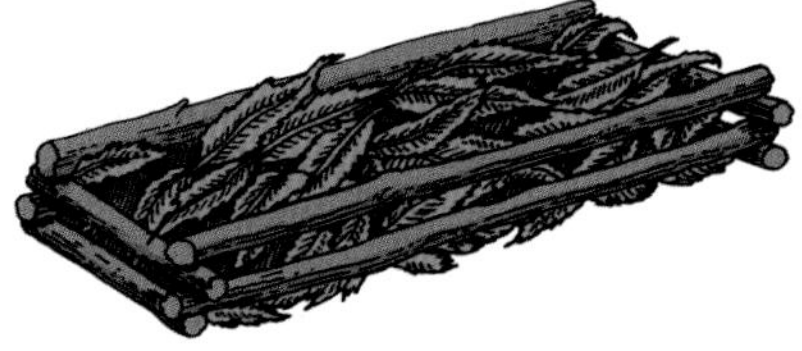

# FINDING WATER AND FOOD

Drinking enough fluid is more important than eating, particularly in hot weather. You need to drink at least two liters of water a day to replace fluids lost naturally. Purify water from rivers, lakes, and streams.

## Collecting water

Collect water from the surface of fast-flowing streams and rivers, if possible, as it will be cleaner. Wade out into a lake to collect water at the surface. Never use a source that looks polluted. Freshly collected rainwater should be pure enough to drink—place containers to catch runoff from tents or roofs.

## Gathering dew

Dew condenses on cold surfaces at dusk and dawn. Mop dew from your tent with a clean cloth or sponge, then wring the moisture into a container. You can also gather water by tying cloths to your ankles and walking through dew-soaked grass.

## Using a transpiration bag

Place a plastic bag over a leafy branch in the sun. Tie the neck securely. Water given off by the leaves will condense and trickle down inside the bag.

## Edible plants

Blackberries, bilberries, wild raspberries, and strawberries are delicious. Rose hips and crab apples are better stewed. Hazelnuts and sweet chestnuts can be roasted. Young, tender leaves of dock, chickweed, and plantain are edible when cooked.

blackberry

wild raspberry

strawberry

hazelnut

crab apples

plantain

sweet chestnut

bilberries

dock leaf

rose hips

chickweed

## Edible fungi

Field and parasol mushrooms are edible when cooked. So are oyster and beefsteak fungus, which grow on trees. You must be 100 percent sure you have identified fungi correctly before eating.

field mushroom

parasol mushroom

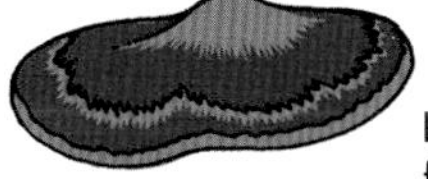
beefsteak fungus

oyster fungus

**BEAR SAYS**

**All water except fresh rainwater must be purified before drinking. You can use a sock to filter debris. Boil water for at least five minutes to kill germs, or use purification tablets.**

## Poisonous fungi

Many fungi are highly poisonous. Beware destroying angel, death cap, and fly agaric. Don't take a chance with fungi—if in doubt, leave it out.

death cap

fly agaric

destroying angel

# GOING FISHING

In summer, rivers will be filled with fish, which are a valuable source of protein, oils, and vitamins. Pretty much all freshwater fish are edible. They are probably the easiest game to catch in a survival situation, but you have to be patient.

## DIY fishing tackle

Rig fishing tackle with nylon line and a hook or safety pin from your mini survival kit. Attach a stick so you can cast away from the bank. Improvise a weight and float. Bait your line with a worm or fish guts—and happy hunting!

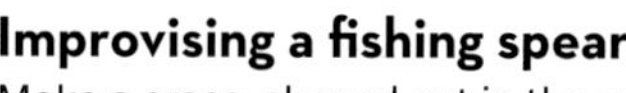

## Improvising a fishing spear

Make a cross-shaped cut in the end of a stout stick or bamboo. The cuts should extend about 6 inches down the shaft. Bind the stick behind the cuts to prevent splitting. Loop string around to separate the prongs, and carve sharp points.

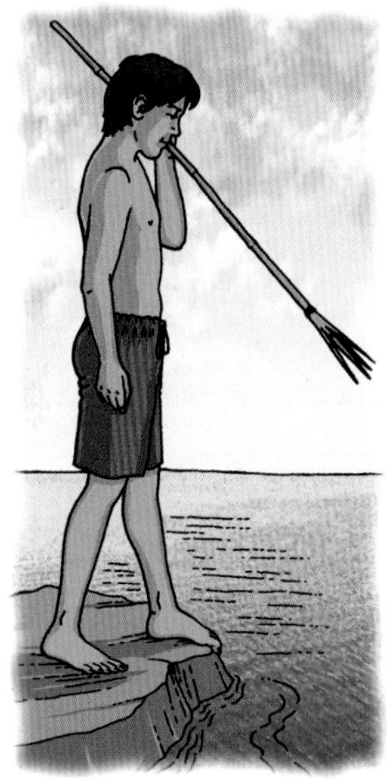

## Spear fishing

Stand on a rock with your spear tip poised just above the surface. Experiment with your aim, as the water's reflection may warp the size and position of the fish. When a fish comes into range, strike to pin the fish to the bottom.

## Making a bottle trap

Cut off the top of a plastic bottle. Insert bait and wedge the top upside down inside the base. Wedge securely among rocks on the bottom. Fish entering to take the bait won't be able to escape.

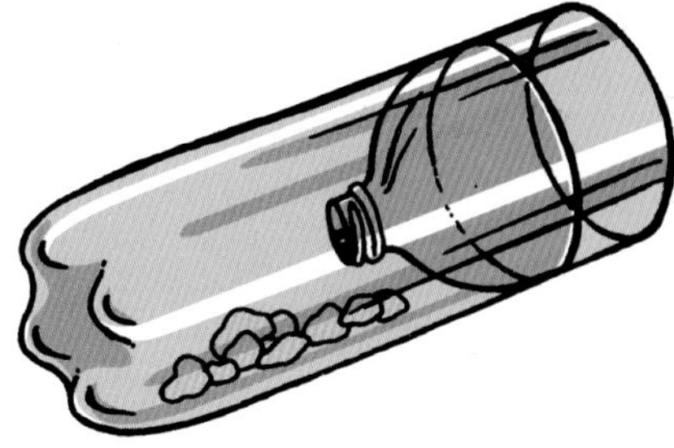

## How to make a fishing weir

Drive sticks into the stream bed to form a trap facing upstream. The sticks must be close together. Use more sticks to create a funnel to direct fish into the trap.

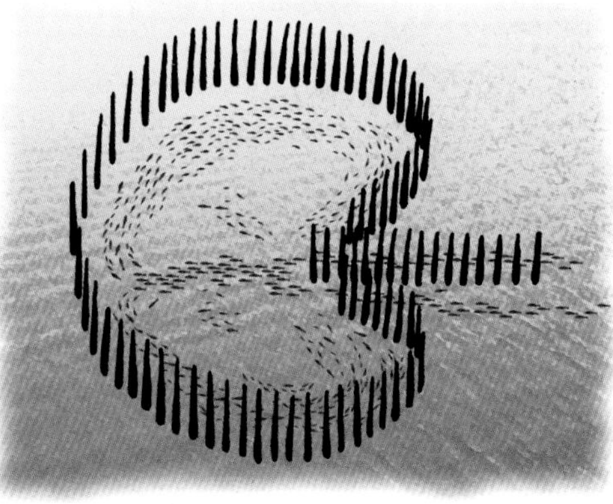

# WILDLIFE WATCHING

Patience is essential if you want to observe wild animals. You've got to be still and quiet to have any chance of getting close to wary creatures. For this reason, warm summer days and evenings are ideal for wildlife watching.

## Tracks

Animals can be identified from the prints they leave in mud or sand. A field guide to local wildlife will show tracks made by animals in your area. Find out when animals are active.

## Trails and traces

Foxes, deer, and other wildlife wear away narrow trails as they forage for food or patrol the borders of their territory. You can also look for food remains such as nibbled shoots, bark, or nuts.

## BEAR SAYS

**Move slowly and stealthily, keeping to cover where possible. Avoid treading on dry twigs or leaves. If spotted, keep absolutely still until the animal relaxes again.**

## Camouflage

Wear dull-colored clothing that blends in with the background to go wildlife watching. You can smear mud to disguise exposed skin such as your face and hands. Leafy twigs stuck in your hat will help disguise your outline.

## Using cover

Often the most effective method is to sit still and let animals approach you. Make as little noise as possible and avoid sudden movements. Hide behind cover such as bushes, trees, or long grass, sit tight, and be prepared to wait.

## Approach downwind

If you approach animals upwind, the breeze will carry your scent and give you away. Test wind direction by holding up a wet finger, or watch foliage moving. Circle to get downwind of animals.

## Leopard crawl

Move forward on all fours, with your weight on knees and elbows. Move your right arm and left leg together, then the opposite pair.

# MAKING A CAMPFIRE

In summer, you may not need a fire for warmth, but you'll need one to cook and boil water. Fire also provides a means of drying clothes and keeping insects and wild animals at bay.

## Science of fire

Fire requires three things: heat, fuel, and oxygen. Remove any one of these and the fire goes out. Use this science to control your fire. For example, smother a fire with earth to remove oxygen if you want it to go out, or add fuel if you want the fire to be stronger.

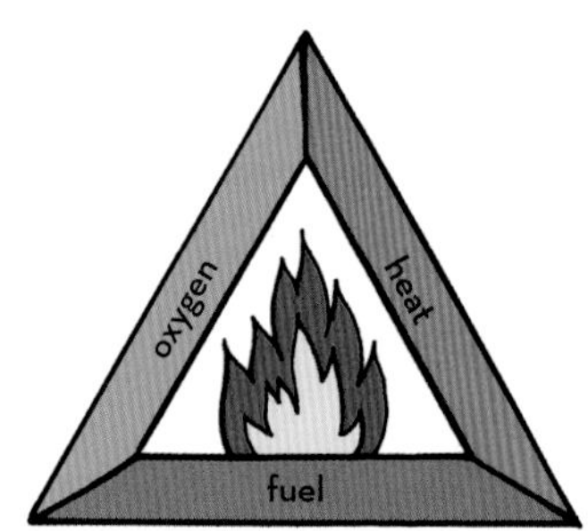


## Gathering fuel

Begin by gathering fuel. You will need dry tinder (such as grasses, birch bark, or wood shavings), kindling (small sticks), and then small and larger logs.

## Building a pyramid fire

A pyramid-shaped fire is easy to light. Make a small pile of tinder, then build kindling in a pyramid above it. A ring of stones or two large logs can be used to contain the fire.

## Fire lighting

The easiest way to light a fire is by using matches or a lighter. Use your body as a wind shield, and cup your hands around the flame. Hold a lighted match sloping downward. Never strike a match toward yourself.

## Using a fire steel

A fire steel creates sparks to ignite tinder. Hold the steel just above the tinder with the striker over it. Draw the striker back against the steel to direct sparks onto the tinder.

**BEAR SAYS**

**Fires are particularly dangerous in hot, dry weather. Stray sparks could easily start a forest fire. Beware drifting sparks, and have water standing by to douse the flames if needed.**

## Using a magnifying glass

In direct sunlight, angle a magnifying glass so light passes through the lens onto the tinder. Smoke will start to rise, then the tinder will ignite.

# CAMP COOKING

Nothing tastes better than food cooked on a campfire after a long day outdoors. You can cook in many different ways—food can be grilled, stewed, fried, roasted, or baked in the embers of your fire.

## Spit roasting

Drive two strong, forked sticks into the ground on either side of the fire. Cut a point in one end of a strong, green (freshly cut) stick and skewer your meat or fish. Place on the spit and turn occasionally so the food cooks evenly.

## Stewing and boiling

Large, flat stones form a firm base for a pan in which you can cook a stew.

## Grilling

Skewers of meat, fish, fruit, or vegetables can be grilled on a barbecue or campfire.

## Making a tripod

A tripod is useful for heating food and boiling water. You need three long, strong, straightish sticks. Bind tightly at one end, then splay the other ends to form the tripod. Suspend a pan or kettle above the fire on a pot hanger (see page 129).

## Using a drying rack

The tripod design can also be used to make a drying rack. Bind three sticks to the struts, and use green, supple twigs to weave a mesh between them. Place thin strips of food on the rack and light a small, smoky fire beneath.

## Making a pot rod

Cut a notch near the end of a strong, freshly cut stick. Wedge it under rocks and over a large log or forked stick to suspend a pot above a fire.

## Baking in foil

Fish, game, potatoes, or fruit can be cooked in foil in the embers of a campfire or barbecue. Wrap the food in foil to create an airtight package. Use tongs to place in the embers, turn, and remove when cooked.

# BUSHCRAFT

Bushcraft is the art of making yourself at home in the wild. With a few simple tools and a little skill you can make all sorts of useful objects that will make camp life more comfortable.

## Making cordage

Cordage is rope, string, or cord. You can make cordage from tough plant fibers such as reeds and vines. You can also use nettles, but crush them first to neutralize the stinging hairs. Roll the fibers between your palms and tie a knot at one end. Join two strands by braiding or rolling in the opposite direction.

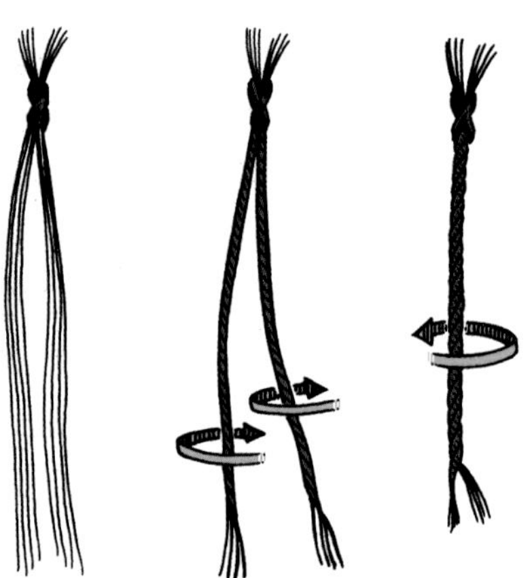

## Tying a reef knot

A reef knot is a very versatile knot. Pass the right end over, then under, the left end. Now pass the left end over and then under the right. Tighten by pulling the two ends.

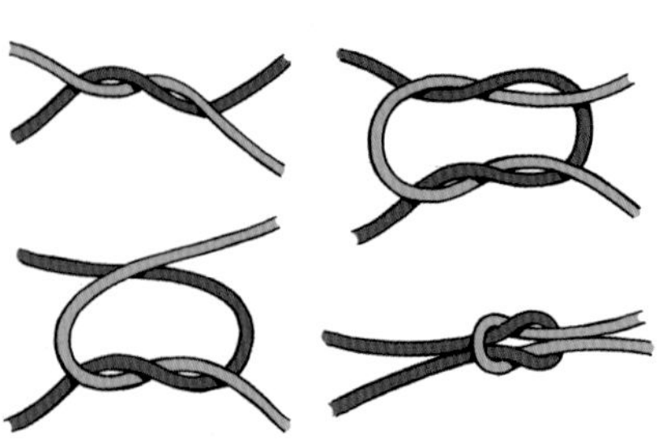

## Tying an overhand knot

Tie an overhand loop to form a fixed loop in a rope. Loop the rope over itself and then pull the loop through the hole.

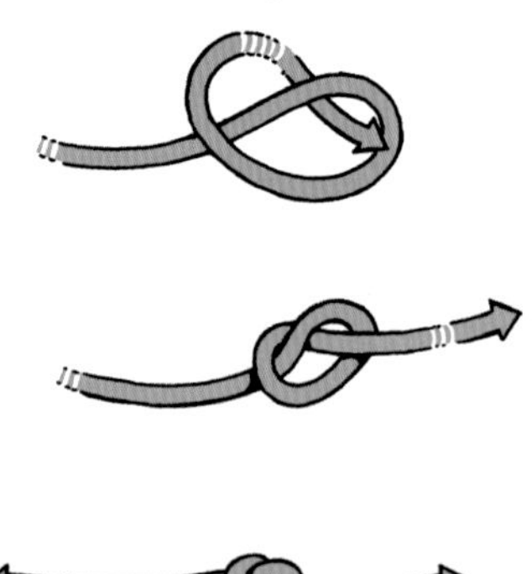

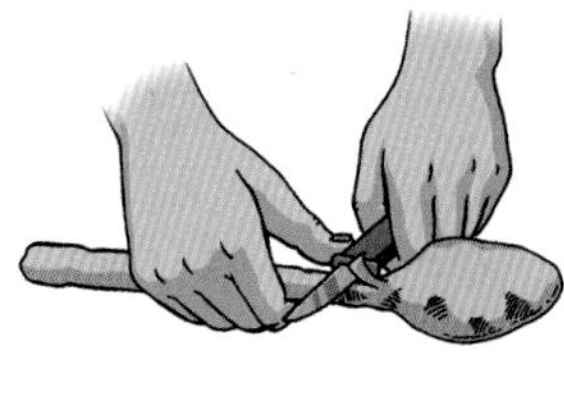

## Carving a wooden spoon

**A hand-carved spoon is a simple craft that provides a lasting memento of time spent in the wild.**

1. Find a dry piece of wood about 10 inches long, 2 inches wide, and 1.5 inches thick. You can also cut and split a larger piece using a saw and hand ax.
2. Use a knife to shape the handle and the back of the bowl. Now trim the sides of the bowl into an oval shape.
3. Hollow out the bowl using a gouging tool or the curved end of your knife. Smooth with a knife or sandpaper.

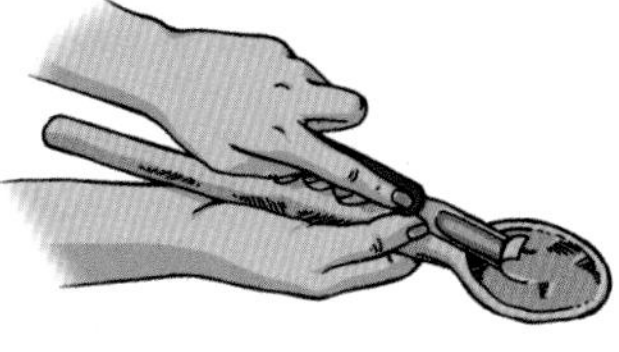

**BEAR SAYS**

**When using a knife, always cut away from your body and fingers. You can use a forehand or backhand grip.**

## Make pot hangers

Pot hangers can be made from forked sticks. Trim the forks to make hooks. Alternatively, you can carve a hook in a straight stick by cutting a neat X-shape with your knife. Pare away the wood from three-quarters of the X. Deepen the notch if required.

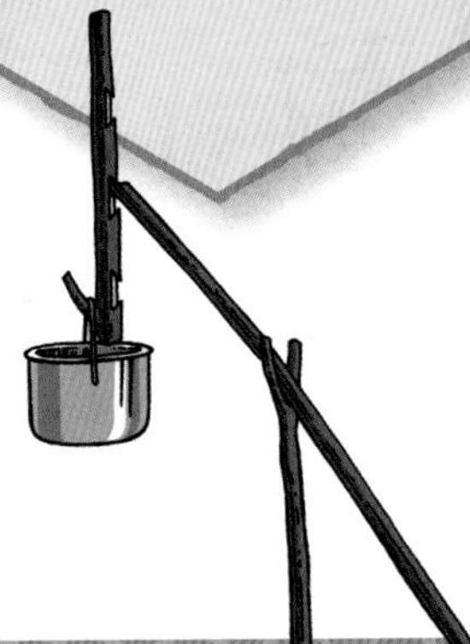

# CAMPFIRE SURVIVAL STORIES

The fire is the heart of any camp. It's a great place to get together and swap stories. Survival tales can provide useful safety tips, and also inspiration for your own adventures.

## Lost in the jungle

In 2007, two men got lost on an 80-mile hike through the Amazon. After running out of food, they survived by eating palm seeds, grubs, and centipedes. They also ate poisonous spiders after cooking them to neutralize the poison. Eventually, after seven weeks in the wild, they made it out alive.

## Island survivor

During World War II, Japanese solider Shoichi Yokoi was posted on a remote Pacific island. He fled into the jungle when enemy troops arrived. Yokoi lived on fruit, snails, fish, and coconuts. He lived in an underground cave, which he dug using a handmade trowel. After an incredible 28 years, he was found, and learned World War II was long over.

## Trapped in a canyon

In 2003, a young hiker was walking in a deep canyon in Utah, when a boulder slipped and trapped his hand. After six days, facing starvation, he cut off his own hand using a multi-tool, and limped to safety.

## Head downstream

In 1971, a teenager was stranded in the Amazon after her plane crashed and she was the only survivor. Alone, she remembered her father's advice to head downstream if you are lost—eventually, you are likely to reach civilization. After nine days, she reached the safety of a hunter's camp, where she dug 50 maggots out of her skin!

## Fluid in the desert

In 1994, an Italian marathon runner got lost in the Sahara Desert during a sandstorm. He survived by drinking his own urine and eating bats and reptiles. After nine days, he finally reached the safety of an oasis.

# ON THE WATER

Summer is the best season to go boating, whether in a canoe, dinghy, raft, or rowboat. The tips on this page will help you stay afloat, and know what to do if you capsize.

## Clothing and equipment

Wear windproof or waterproof clothing, and deck shoes or plastic sandals. Vital safety gear should include a life jacket and helmet for white water. Take rope, a container to bail with, and dry clothes in a sealed plastic bag.

life jacket

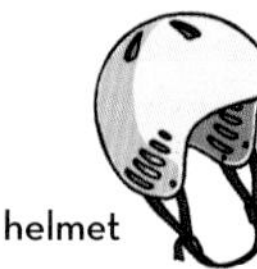

helmet

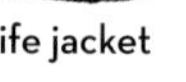

rope

sunscreen

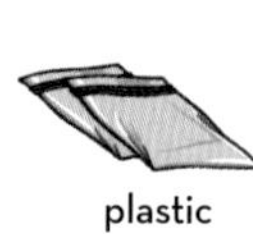

plastic bags

bucket

deck shoes

waterproof jacket

## Preparation

Before you set off, check tide times and wind speeds and direction. Check the forecast for hazards such as fog, mist, and squalls.

### DOs and DON'Ts

**DO** wear a life jacket.

**DO** be courteous to other water users.

**DON'T** overload your craft with gear or people. Stow all gear securely.

**DON'T** ignore a bad weather forecast or problems such as leaks.

## Kayak capsize

A technique called an Eskimo roll rights a kayak that has overturned. You use the paddle as a lever and twist your hips to flip the boat upright. It takes skill and practice. If you haven't mastered this trick, practice exiting an overturned kayak by lifting the spray deck, grabbing the rim, and pushing yourself out.

## Righting a dinghy

Brace your feet against the hull and pull on a rope or the daggerboard. Walk over the hull as the craft rights itself. If you can't right your vessel, stay with it, as you will be much easier to spot.

## In the water

If your boat sinks in open water, don't exhaust yourself swimming. Just stay afloat by treading water. Keep your body upright and move your arms and legs in small circles. If wearing a life jacket, conserve body heat by crossing your arms and legs.

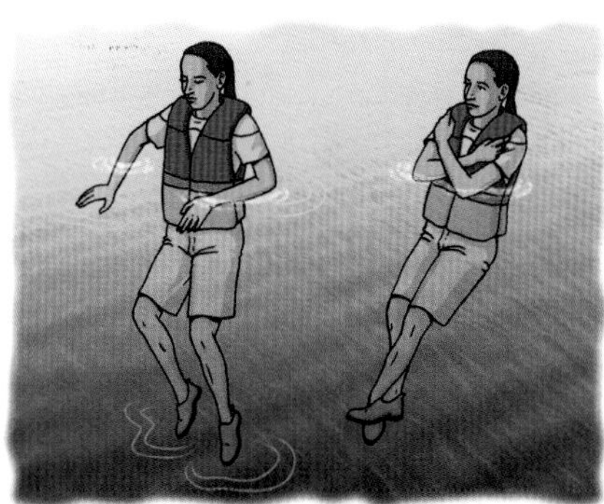

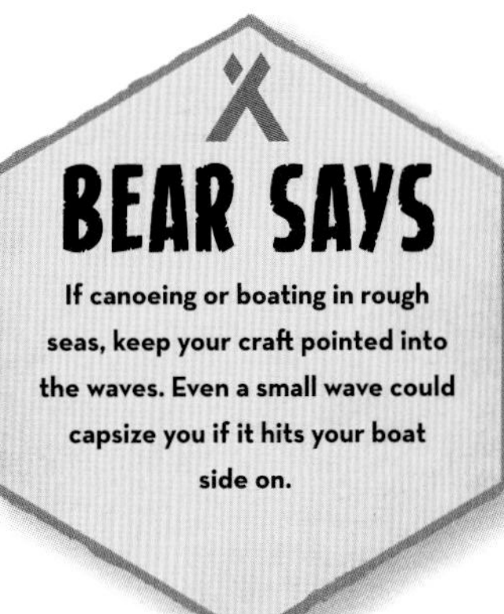

**BEAR SAYS**

**If canoeing or boating in rough seas, keep your craft pointed into the waves. Even a small wave could capsize you if it hits your boat side on.**

# BUILDING A RAFT

Rafts are one of the very oldest forms of water transportation. With rope and some timber, you can practice the ancient art of raft building. In a survival situation, you can use a raft to escape from dense jungle or a desert island.

### Building a driftwood raft

1. Scout along the shore for materials such as driftwood, rope, netting, and floats. Lash long wood pieces together with rope to form the base of the raft. Tie all knots tightly.
2. Lash more wood at right angles to the first layer. If you have an ax, cut notches in the base for these cross struts.
3. Test the raft for buoyancy. Floating objects can be lashed to the underside to improve buoyancy.
4. Rafts are hard to steer. Use a plank for a rudder—lash it to an A-frame near the stern.
5. If desired, you can raise a mast and add canvas, plastic sheeting, or woven leaves to provide shade and a sail.
6. Use spare wood to make a paddle. In shallow water, you can punt with a pole.

## Bamboo raft

Bamboo is an excellent material for raft building. Cut poles about 10 ft. long, using a machete. Use the point of a knife to make two lines of holes through the poles. Thread rope or thin canes through the holes to lash the raft together. Add a second layer of poles.

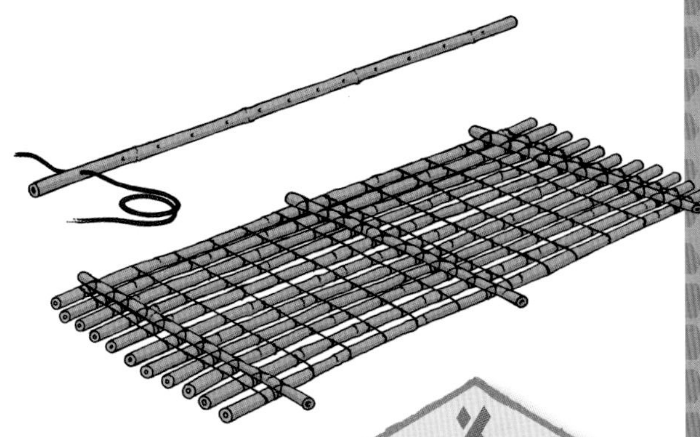

## BEAR SAYS

**Build your raft close to the water's edge so it can be launched easily, but beware changing water levels due to rainfall or tides.**

## Before launching

Check winds, waves, tides, and currents before launching. If you have a map, scan for hazards such as reefs, shoals, and rapids. On a river, watch for overhanging branches. Listen for the sound of crashing water, which could indicate a waterfall ahead.

# WILD SWIMMING

Swimming in places such as lakes, rivers, and the ocean is known as wild swimming. Warm air and water temperatures make summer the best time for swimming. Knowing how to swim strongly and safely is a vital survival skill.

## Swimwear and gear

A wet suit, gloves, and swim cap may be needed for long-distance and cold-water swimming. Goggles and a whistle will come in handy. Plastic shoes make it easier to enter and leave the water. Don't forget your towel!

towel

goggles

swim cap

whistle

plastic shoes

gloves

wet suit

### DOs and DON'Ts

**DO** keep track of your position in the sea or a river. Notice which way you are drifting and don't get swept away.

**DO** watch for overhanging branches that could pull you under in a swift current.

**DON'T** swim alone or at night.

**DON'T** dive off rocks into water of uncertain depth.

## Preparation

As with boating, check currents and tides, wind speeds, and direction. Don't swim in stormy weather. Beware steep banks and thick mud along rivers. Weeds and other floating objects show where the current is flowing fast.

## Offshore currents

If you are swept offshore by a current, don't try to swim directly against it. Swim diagonally to shore, or float along the coast until the current slackens, then make for land.

## Swimming in surf

Strong surf can create a powerful undertow. Face the waves. Dive under breakers and surface once the wave has passed. Beware reefs and rocks.

## BEAR SAYS

**Don't swim close to boats with outboard motors. Whirling propellers are very dangerous. Give all craft a wide berth, and make sure other water users have seen you.**

## Escaping from a whirlpool

Whirlpools can form below weirs and dams, or where currents meet offshore. If caught in a whirlpool, don't panic. If you go with the flow, the current may slacken. Or take a deep breath and dive down—the current may weaken or throw you out.

# ON THE BEACH

For many people, summer means going to the beach. In a survival situation, beaches are great places to find food and rig a shelter. However, tides, currents, and some sea creatures can be dangerous, so it always pays to take care.

## Tides and currents

Water levels on many beaches change dramatically as tides rise and fall. Tides can also create strong offshore currents. Find out what the tide is doing. Don't get cut off by a rising tide.

## Foraging

Seashores contain abundant food if you know where to look for it. Hunt for fish, shrimp, and crabs in rock pools, and pry limpets off rocks using a penknife. Seaweeds such as kelp and sea lettuce taste great in a seafood casserole.

## Cracking a coconut

Coconuts are a valuable food source. Ram the coconut "eye" onto a sharpened stake. Drink the fluid, then crack the nut open and eat the flesh.

## Beachcombing

In a survival situation, check along the tide line for useful debris such as bottles, containers, nets, and floats—and, of course, driftwood to build a fire.

## Caves

Caves can offer shelter on a beach, but before moving in, you have to be absolutely sure the cave won't fill with water at high tide. Check the cave walls for signs of rising tides and damp.

## Rigging a beach shelter

Site your shelter above the high tide mark. Make an A-frame by lashing wooden spars together. Push the ends into the sand. Tie on a ridgepole sloping downward, then lay sticks vertically against the ridgepole. Use thorns or string to secure large leaves to form a thatch.

## BEAR SAYS

**Beware sea snakes, jellyfish, and sharks. While most jellyfish stings are painful but not dangerous, the sting of a box jellyfish can be fatal.**

# WEATHER WATCHING

Adventuring in different kinds of weather can be fun, but all weathers present their own problems. It's important to know how to predict what the weather is going to do, and how to stay safe. Then you can go into the wild knowing you are prepared for anything!

Bear

# IN THIS SECTION:

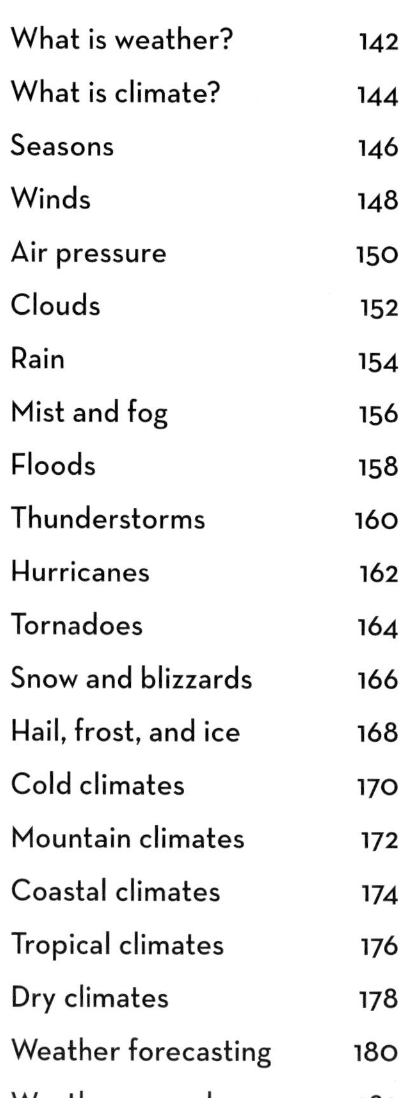

# WHAT IS WEATHER?

Weather means the different conditions outside—whether it's warm or chilly, sunny or cloudy, dry or rainy. Weather affects all outdoor activities, so understanding the weather is a vital survival skill.

### What causes weather?

All the weather conditions we experience are caused by the sun heating the air in different places by different amounts. The oceans also affect the weather (see pages 174–175).

### Rainfall

Falling moisture, such as rain, is called precipitation.

### Sunshine

The sun's heat causes moisture to rise from the oceans, producing clouds.

### Temperature

The temperature is how warm or cold the air is. Snow falls when the air is cold.

### Be prepared!

Prepare for all kinds of weather on outdoor expeditions by bringing several layers of clothing. Take off a layer if you are hot, and put one on if you are cold. Take a rain or sun hat, or a beanie, depending on the weather.

You will also need:

1. Waterproof jacket in case of rain
2. Gloves
3. Boots or walking shoes
4. Watch
5. Rucksack

Take these items on all expeditions:

1. Drink and snack
2. First aid kit
3. Flashlight
4. Mobile phone
5. Map and compass

## Earth's atmosphere

Weather happens in Earth's atmosphere—a blanket of gases that surrounds the planet. The atmosphere has five main layers: the exosphere, thermosphere, mesosphere, stratosphere, and troposphere.

**BEAR SAYS**

**Checking the weather forecast is a vital part of planning for hikes and expeditions. Check the forecast online, on TV, or on the radio.**

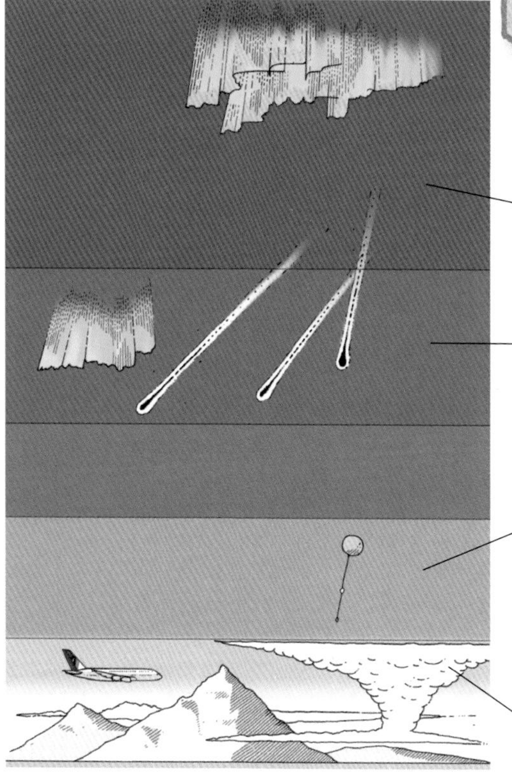

The exosphere contains very little gas and fades away into space.

Colored lights called auroras can be seen in the thermosphere (and exosphere).

The stratosphere contains a thin layer of ozone gas, which screens out harmful ultraviolet rays in sunlight. Planes fly in this calm layer.

Weather happens in the lowest layer, the troposphere, which also contains most gases.

## Sunscreen

In the twentieth century, air pollution made the ozone layer thinner, allowing harmful ultraviolet light through. Wear sunscreen outdoors to protect your skin.

# WHAT IS CLIMATE?

Climate is not the same as weather. In many places the weather changes constantly. The climate is the bigger picture—the average weather conditions, as recorded over many years.

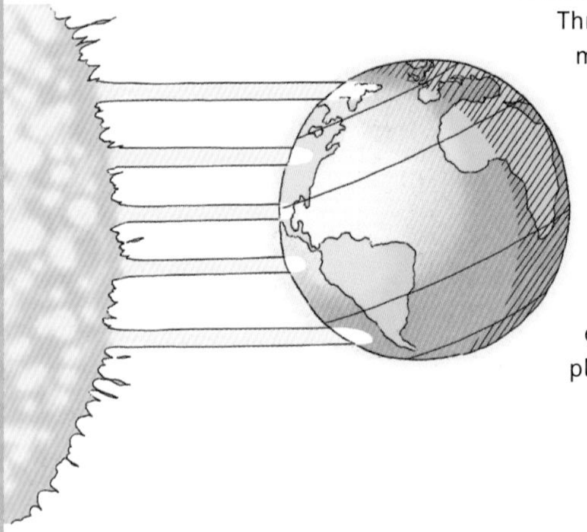

### What causes climate?

Three main factors affect climate. The most important is distance from the equator (an imaginary line that runs around Earth's center). The sun's rays beat down directly in tropical regions close to the equator, so the climate here is always hot. They strike less directly in regions farther north and south because of Earth's curving surface, so these places are cooler.

### Altitude

Height above sea level also affects climate. The air higher up holds less of the sun's heat, so mountains are cooler than lowlands (see pages 172–173).

### Distance from coast

Coastal regions have a milder climate than places far inland. This is because the sea cools the land in summer and warms it in winter (see pages 174–175).

## Climate zones

Each part of Earth has a particular climate. The main climate zones are shown on the map below. Research a region's climate if you plan a trip abroad, so you know what to pack.

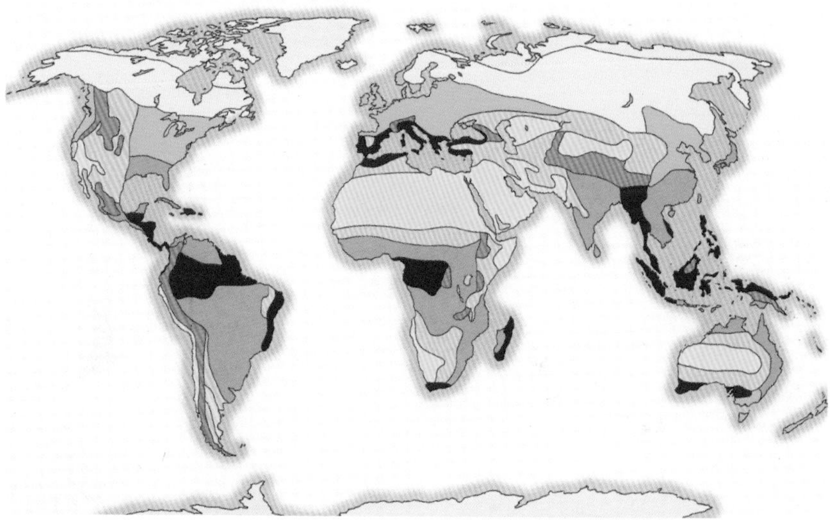

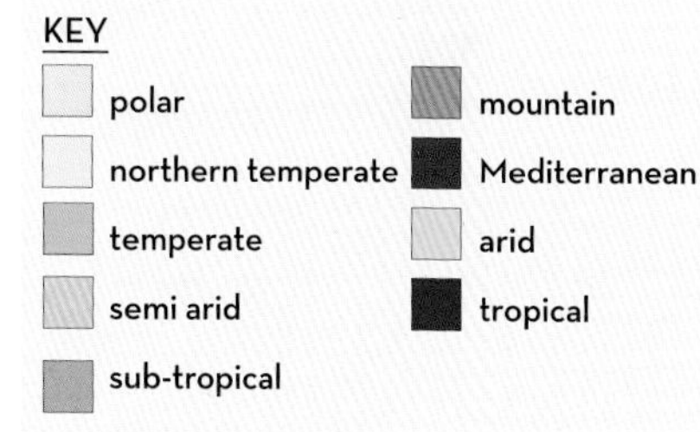


## Microclimates

Small areas such as cities may have a slightly different climate than their surroundings. This is called a microclimate. Cities are warmer because buildings and roads trap heat.

## Climate change

Temperatures worldwide are now rising because air pollution is trapping the sun's heat in the atmosphere. Global warming is starting to affect environments worldwide.

# SEASONS

Many parts of Earth have a climate that varies at different times of year. These regular changes, seasons, happen because Earth tilts on its axis (an imaginary line between the North and South Pole) as it circles the sun.

### What causes seasons?

Earth tilts 23.5 degrees on its axis. The tilt always points the same way in space. When one half of Earth leans toward the sun, it has summer, and the other half has winter. Six months later, the seasons are reversed.

**Understanding the seasons helps survival experts plan expeditions. Explorers visit the poles in summer when it's light 24 hours a day.**

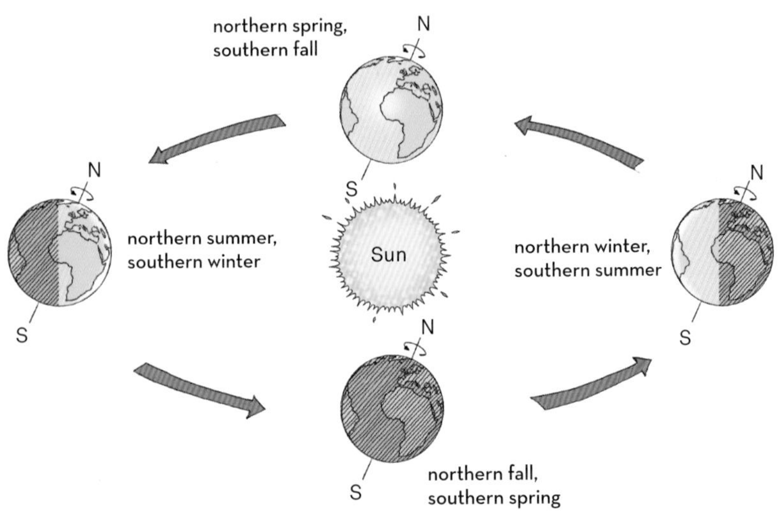

### Tropical rainfall

Many parts of the tropics are wet year round. Tropical rain forests grow here.

### Wet and dry

Some parts of the tropics have two seasons—a dry season and a rainy season.

## Temperate climate throughout the year

Temperate regions lying between the tropics and the poles experience four distinct seasons: spring, summer, fall, and winter.

### Spring

Broad-leaved trees sprout new leaves in spring, when temperatures start to rise.

### Summer

Plants grow quickly in summer, when temperatures are warmest.

### Fall

Broad-leaved trees shed their leaves in fall to prepare for winter.

### Winter

Broad-leaved trees are bare of leaves in winter, the coldest season.

## Polar climate

The polar regions experience extreme seasons. In winter, each pole tilts away from the sun. It is dark all day and bitterly cold. In summer, each pole tilts toward the sun. It is light all day and all night, but temperatures are still cool.

# WINDS

Winds are currents of moving air. The sun's heat produces wind by heating air in different places unevenly. Air warmed by the sun becomes less dense, so it rises. Cooler, denser air moves in to replace it, making a wind.

### Earth's winds

Warm air rises near the equator and flows toward the poles. Cooler polar air rushes in to replace it. This produces circulating wind patterns called wind cells. But winds are also bent by Earth's rotation. This produces regular wind patterns called prevailing winds.

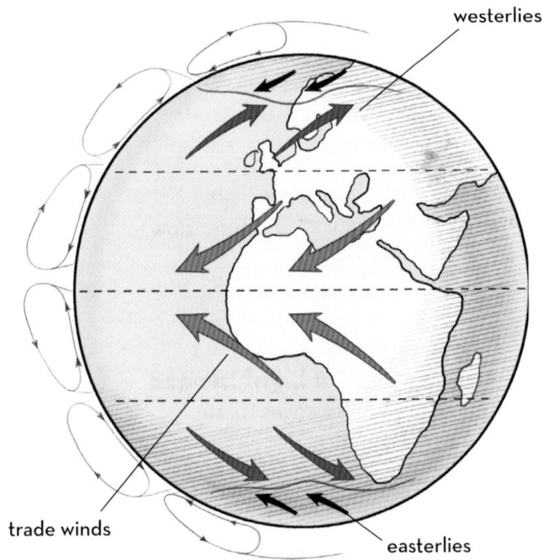


### Wind chill

Wind blows away your body heat, making the air feel colder. This is called wind chill. See the tables on page 29 or 57 to see how temperatures drop depending on wind speed.

**BEAR SAYS**

**When hiking in windy weather, take breaks in sheltered places, such as behind a wall. Avoid exposed places such as ridges, where a gust of wind could blow you off your feet.**

## Beaufort scale

The Beaufort scale measures wind speeds according to its effect on trees, smoke, buildings, and waves at sea.

**0 Calm**
No wind, smoke rises vertically.

**1 Light air**
Smoke drifts slowly.

**2 Light breeze**
Leaves rustle.

**3 Gentle breeze**
Twigs and leaves move.

**4 Moderate breeze**
Small branches move.

**5 Fresh breeze**
Small trees sway.

**6 Strong breeze**
Large branches sway.

**7 Near gale**
Trees sway.

**8 Gale**
Twigs snap. It's hard to walk.

**9 Severe gale**
Branches break, tiles blow off roofs.

**10 Storm**
Trees are uprooted.

**11 Violent storm**
Widespread damage.

**12 Hurricane**
Widespread destruction.

# AIR PRESSURE

Air pressure is the weight of all the air pressing down on us. Differences in air pressure produce weather systems called fronts, which may bring clouds, rain, or storms.

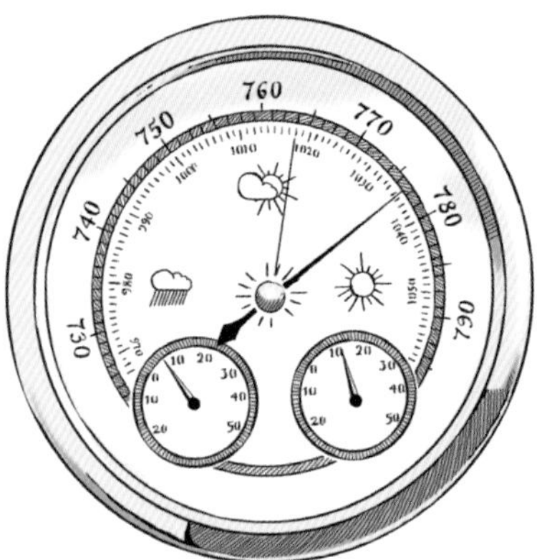


## Measuring air pressure

Instruments called barometers measure air pressure. They also predict the weather. Rising air pressure often brings fine, dry weather. Falling air pressure often produces clouds and rain.

## Highs and lows

Warm air rises, producing a "low," or area of air at low pressure, at ground level. Air swirls around the low-pressure center and is sucked in and upward. Sinking cold air produces a "high" of denser air at high pressure. The cold air warms, preventing moisture from condensing, which often produces dry weather.

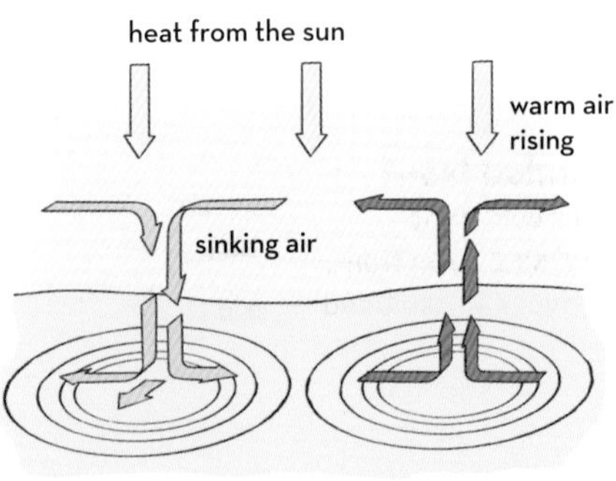

## Weather fronts

Weather fronts are zones where warm and cold air meet. The front is named after the temperature of the advancing air. These systems are shown on weather maps (see page 181).

### Cold front

An advancing mass of cold air burrows below warm air, which rises quickly. Moisture condenses. Strong winds and showers are often followed by fine, dry weather.

### Warm front

A warm air mass slides over denser, colder air. A sequence of different clouds may be seen.

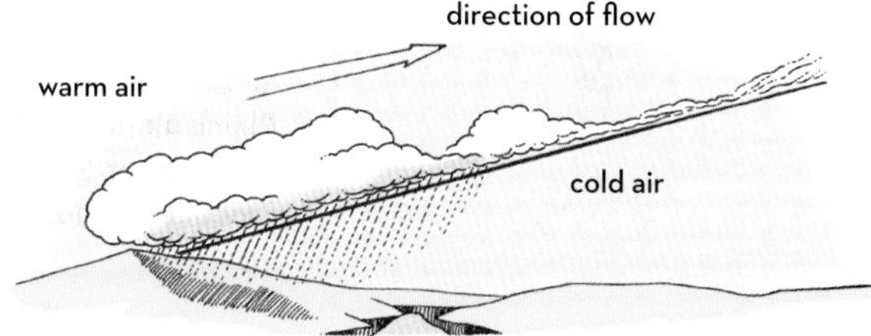


### Occluded front

When a cold front overtakes a warm front, it produces an occluded front. The cold air lifts the warm air off the ground, producing clouds and rain.

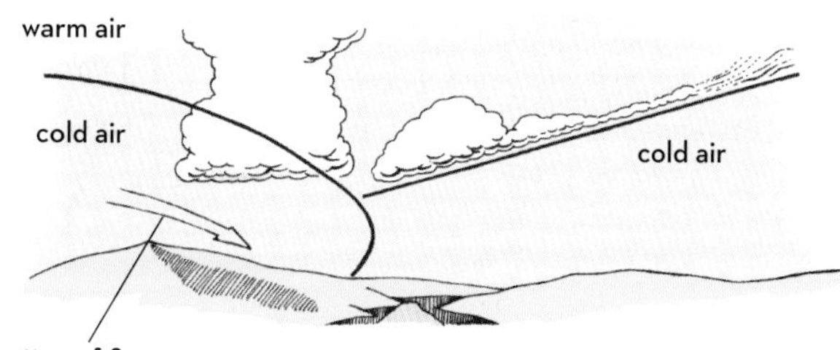

# CLOUDS

Clouds are floating masses of moisture—either tiny water droplets or ice crystals. Different types of clouds suggest that fine weather, storms, or rain are on the way, so recognizing clouds is an important survival skill.

**BEAR SAYS**

**Clouds shield us from the sun's heat and the harmful ultraviolet rays in sunlight. At night, they produce warmer temperatures, but, of course, they can also bring rain!**

cumulus

cumulonimbus

cirrus

cirrocumulus

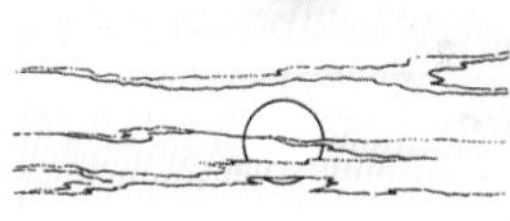

cirrostratus

altocumulus

stratus

stratocumulus

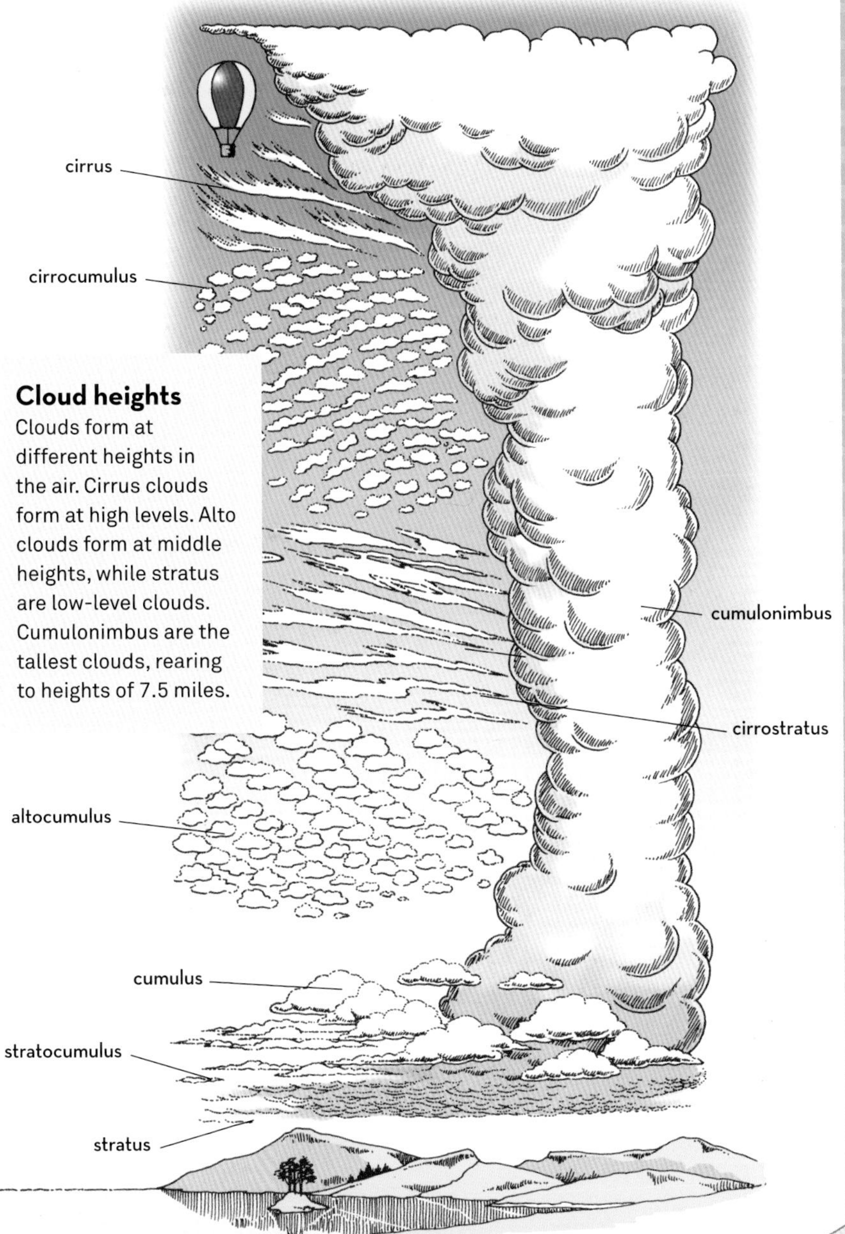


## Cloud heights

Clouds form at different heights in the air. Cirrus clouds form at high levels. Alto clouds form at middle heights, while stratus are low-level clouds. Cumulonimbus are the tallest clouds, rearing to heights of 7.5 miles.

# RAIN

All the moisture in clouds eventually falls as liquid rain, or icy hail or snow. Falling moisture is called precipitation. For outdoor activities, be prepared for rain even if the weather is fine.

## Why it rains

Tiny floating water droplets in clouds are blown about by air currents. They collide and join to form bigger droplets or crystals. Eventually they get too heavy to float on air, so they fall to the ground.

## Water cycle

Water circles between the air, land, and oceans. We call this the water cycle.

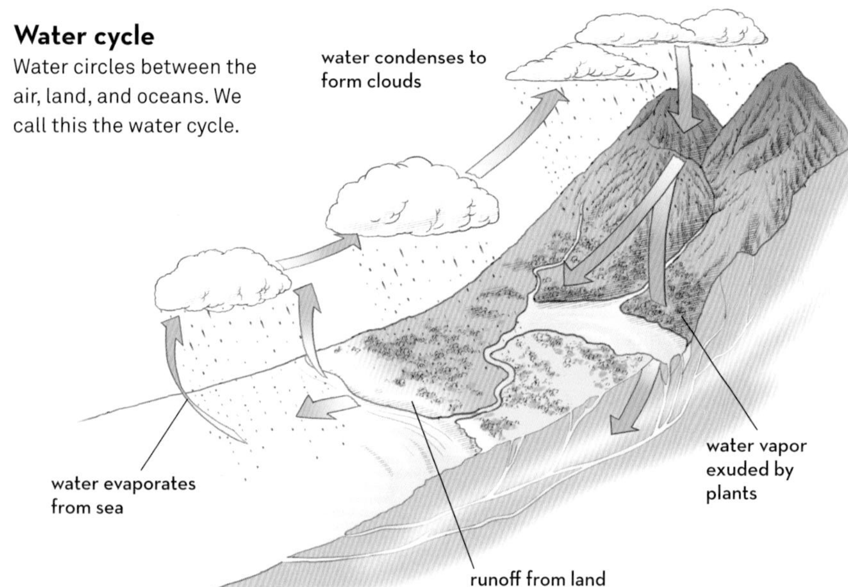


## Rainfall patterns

Different parts of the world receive very different levels of rainfall. In some places rain is abundant, while regions such as deserts are very dry.

## Rain shadow areas

Mountain slopes facing wet winds blowing off the ocean get a lot of rain. But the air has shed its moisture by the time it reaches the far side of the mountain, producing a dry zone called a rain shadow.

## Wet weather gear

Wet clothing will chill you and can even produce hypothermia. Modern rainwear is often made of "breathable" fabric, which allows sweat to pass through while keeping you dry. Avoid wearing jeans, which soak up a lot of moisture and then take a long time to dry out.

## Rainbows

Rainbows form when the sun shines through raindrops. As white light passes through each raindrop it is bent and split into many colors—red, orange, yellow, green, blue, indigo, and violet.

**BEAR SAYS**

**Line your rucksack with a plastic bag to keep the contents dry. Or buy a plastic rucksack cover—some rucksacks are supplied with a cover.**

# MIST AND FOG

Mist and fog are low-lying cloud. When they appear quickly, it's all too easy to lose your bearings. Knowing how to read a compass is vital in these dangerous conditions.

## Mist or fog

If you can see 0.5–2 miles through low cloud, it is called mist. If you can see less than 0.5 miles, it is called fog.

Golden Gate Bridge, San Francisco, CA

## Forming and clearing

Fog and mist form when moist air cools as it contacts cold surfaces, such as ground or water, and moisture condenses. This often happens at night. Fog and mist clear in the morning as the sun warms the air because warm air can hold more moisture than cold air.

## Map and compass

Use a map and a compass to find your way even in thick fog. This technique is called setting the map.

1. Lay the compass flat on the map. Line up the edge of the compass with the direction you are headed on the map.

2. Turn the round compass dial so the vertical lines on the dial line up with the gridlines on the map, with the red dial arrow pointing north on the map.

3. Take the compass off the map and hold it level. Turn your body around until the red magnetic needle lines up with the dial arrow. The black direction of travel arrow at the front shows you which way to go.

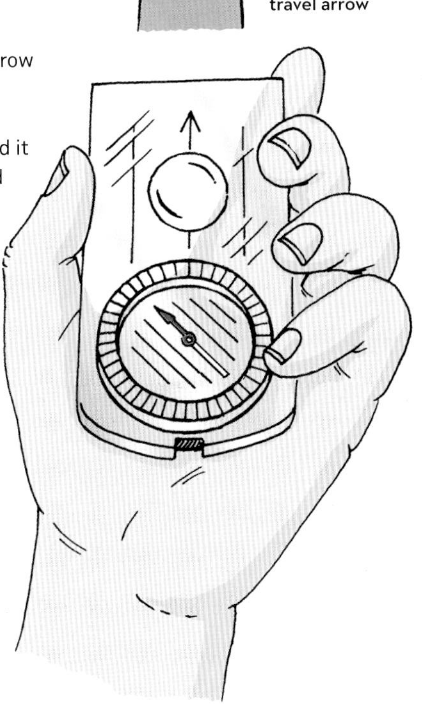


**BEAR SAYS**

**Mist and fog can descend with little warning. In just minutes, all landmarks can be blotted out. Keep calm and get your compass out!**

# FLOODS

Flooding can be a danger after heavy rain and thunderstorms. Rainwater quickly swells streams and rivers, turning them into raging torrents.

## Types of floods

There are two main types of floods—river and coastal. Rivers burst their banks after heavy rain. Coastal floods strike during high tides, storms, and hurricanes, or they may be caused by tsunamis (giant waves).

## Monsoon rains

Tropical countries such as India lie in the path of monsoon winds that change direction at different times of year. Floods often strike in the rainy season.

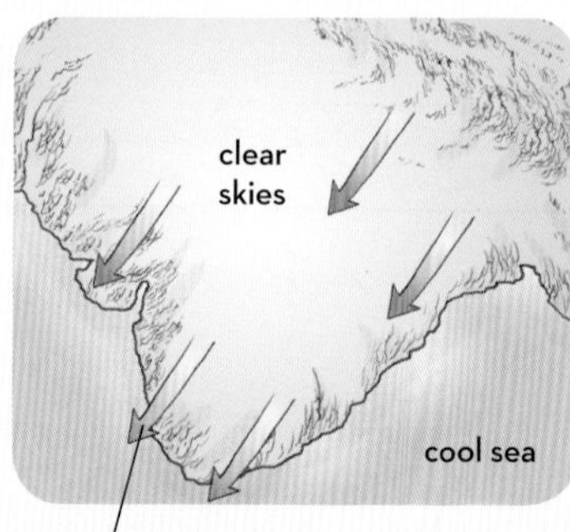

## Flash floods

Flash floods strike in deep canyons and valleys below hills and mountains. After a cloudburst, rainwater swells streams, sending a wall of water surging downhill. Water levels rise quickly, sweeping away trees, roads, bridges, cars, and livestock.

## River crossings

Scan for the safest place before attempting a river crossing. A fallen tree may provide a natural bridge, or boulders may form stepping stones. Don't try to cross fast-running water that is higher than your knees.

If there are two of you, link arms or hold onto a backpack.

A stout stick provides extra support when crossing a swollen stream. You can also use the stick to check the water depth.

If there are three of you, link arms to form a circle. Cross with the strongest or heaviest person upstream.

# THUNDERSTORMS

Thunderstorms are the most common form of extreme weather. In hot, sticky conditions, thunderstorms can strike daily, bringing danger in the form of lightning, high winds, and heavy rain.

## Why thunderstorms strike

Electric charges build up inside thunderclouds as winds cause water droplets, ice crystals, and hail to rub together. The top of the cloud develops a positive charge. The base of the cloud becomes negatively charged, while a positive charge also builds up on the ground below.

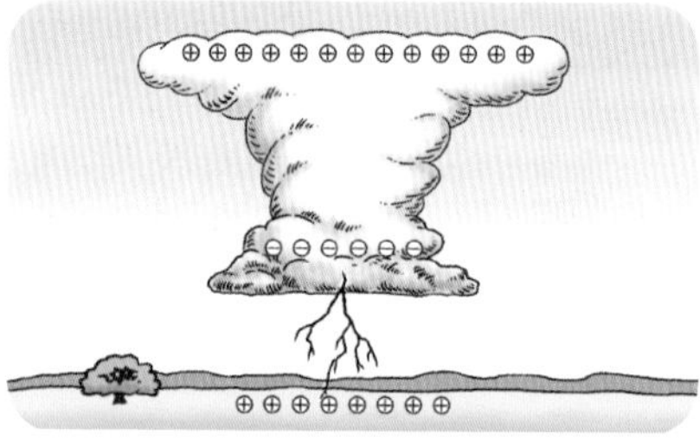

**BEAR SAYS**

**If possible, it's best to avoid being caught in the open when a thunderstorm strikes. Check weather reports before you go, and if it looks like it might be stormy, stay home.**

## Types of lightning

When the charge is great enough, electric sparks are released. Lightning can flash inside a thundercloud or from a cloud to the ground (shown below). It can also jump between two storm clouds.

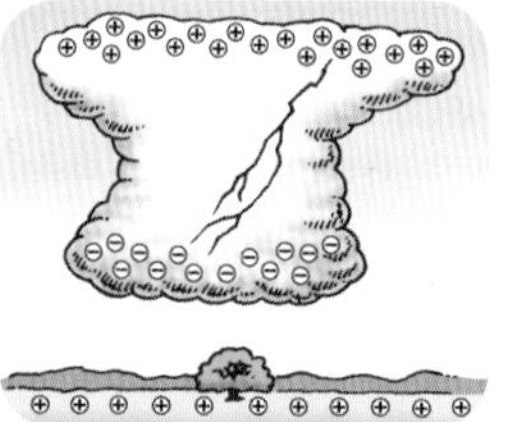

intracloud lightning

cloud-to-ground lightning

### Places to avoid in a storm

**High ground**
Avoid exposed ridges and mountaintops during storms.

**Lone trees**
Never shelter under a single tall tree, which could attract lightning.

**Picnic shelter**
A picnic shelter offers little protection in a storm.

## Places to shelter

**Car**
Cars are fairly safe places. Close windows and avoid touching metal.

**Grove**
A thicket of shrubs or low trees is relatively safe if there are taller trees nearby.

**Down low**
A gully offers protection against lightning, but may flood after heavy rain.

**Safety tips**
Discard metal objects such as walking poles or umbrellas. If you are swimming, get out of the water as quickly as possible.

**Crouching position**
Crouch low with your hands protecting your head and covering your ears. If lightning strikes, the current should pass through your feet, not your upper body.

# HURRICANES

Hurricanes are vast, spinning storms that begin out over the sea in the tropics. They are incredibly dangerous, bringing winds of up to 200 mph, which can uproot trees and rip buildings off their foundations.

## How hurricanes form

Hurricanes form over tropical oceans in warm, sticky weather. As a group of thunderstorms combine, warm, moist air shoots upward and starts to spiral.

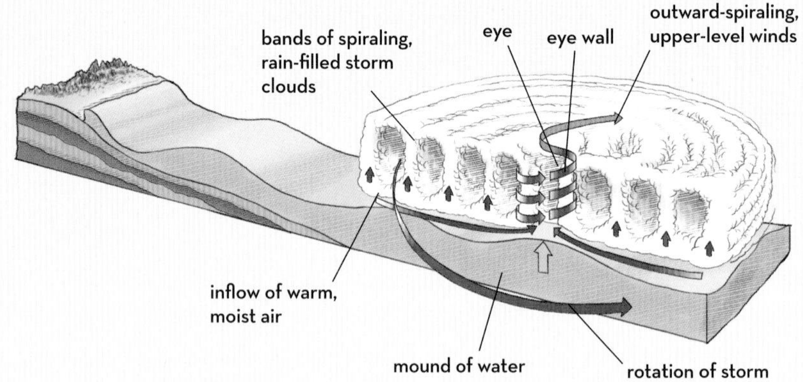


## Eye of the storm

From space, a hurricane resembles a whirling Catherine wheel of cloud, spinning around a calm central area called the eye.

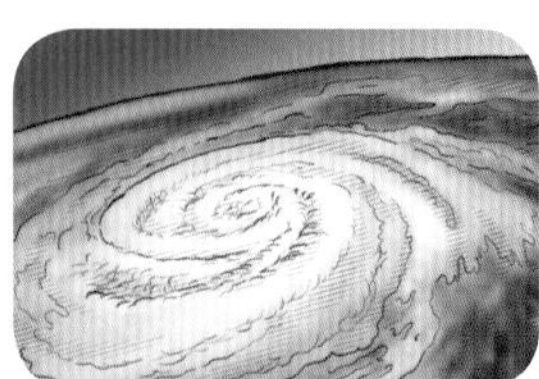

## Storm surge

The low-pressure zone in the eye sucks up water, which heaps up below it. When this mound, called a storm surge, hits the coast, it causes floods.

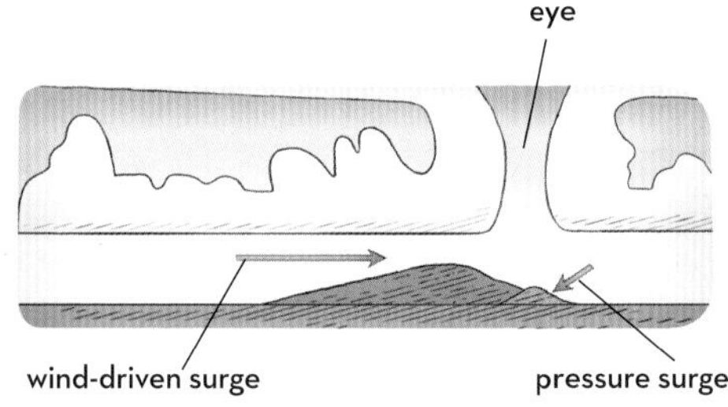

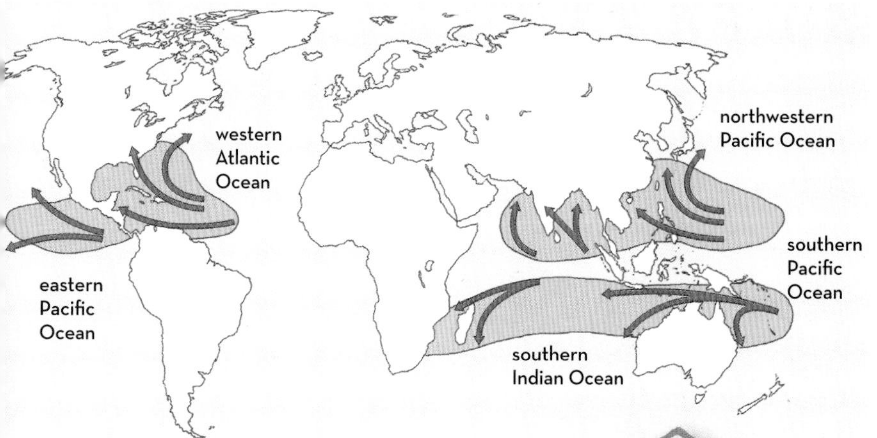


## Hurricane danger zones

Hurricanes form over warm oceans. In the Indian Ocean they are called tropical cyclones, in the western Pacific they are called typhoons.

## Preparation

Weather experts carefully monitor storms in the hurricane season. If needed, the authorities issue warnings. They may order people to take shelter, or even leave the area.

**BEAR SAYS**

**Heed all weather warnings. Never go outside if a hurricane is due. Shelter in a sturdy building, away from areas at risk of flooding.**

## Storm preparation

People may board up their windows to avoid glass being shattered, and move important household items to higher ground in case of flooding.

## Devastation

Hurricanes can cause devastation. People are only allowed to return when it is safe.

# TORNADOES

Tornadoes, or "twisters," are whirling funnels of air. They are far smaller than hurricanes but contain even more powerful, spinning winds.

**BEAR SAYS**

**Watch for a funnel of air forming below thunderclouds. If you are in a car, drive in the opposite direction, or take shelter fast!**

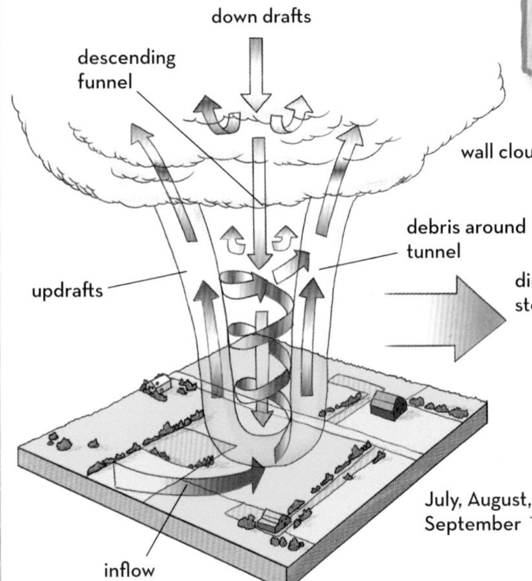


July, August, September

April, May, June

January, February, March

### How do tornadoes form?

Tornadoes form over land beneath violent storm clouds called supercells. As warm air rises rapidly and starts spinning, a funnel of whirling air forms below the cloud, and touches down as a tornado.

### Tornado Alley

Tornadoes commonly strike in the southern/central US, in a wide band called Tornado Alley. Sometimes many tornadoes form—these groups are called swarms.

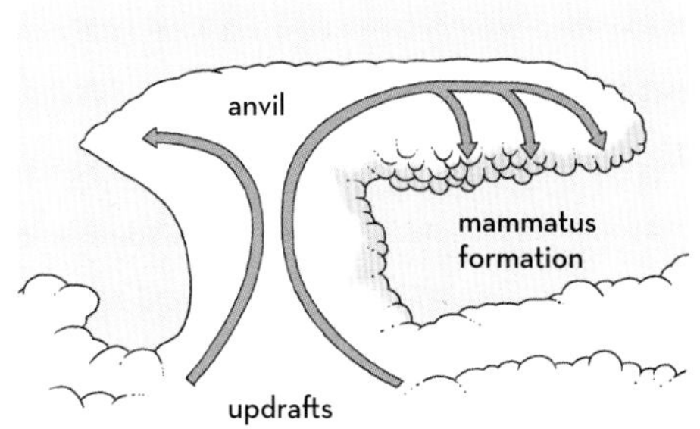


## Mammatus clouds

Weird bulging clouds called mammatus clouds sometimes appear before tornadoes form.

## Dust devils

In deserts, spinning winds can pick up dust to form small whirlwinds called dust devils. Shield your eyes, nose, and mouth from flying sand and grit.

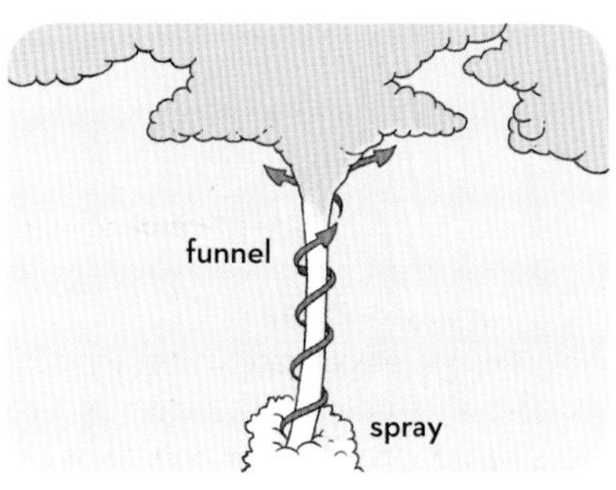


## Waterspouts

Spinning winds at sea sometimes suck up water to form a funnel called a waterspout. These whirling columns don't usually last long.

# SNOW AND BLIZZARDS

Snow forms when moisture freezes in very low temperatures. When strong winds blow during a heavy snowfall, it is called a blizzard.

### Gear and clothing

Wear several layers of warm clothing including a thermal under layer. The top layer should be waterproof. You'll also need boots, gloves, a scarf, and a hat or balaclava to prevent heat loss from your head.

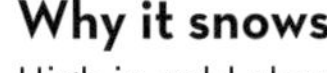

### Why it snows

High in cold clouds, winds blow ice crystals together. They combine to make snowflakes, which eventually get so big and heavy they cannot float, so they drift to the ground.

### Power cuts

Heavy snow can bring power lines down, causing outages. Heavy snow can break branches, trees, and roofs.

## BEAR SAYS

**In a blizzard, wind drives snow into every gap in your clothing. Make sure you are zipped and buttoned up before going outdoors.**

### Snowdrifts

Wind blows snow into deep drifts that can block roads. If stuck in a car, run the engine as little as possible. Open a window a little to allow fresh air inside.

## Building a snow hole

A snow hole will keep you alive if caught outdoors overnight without shelter. You need a deep snowdrift and a shovel. Dig a tunnel heading slightly downward and then upward. Hollow out a space at the end, packing down the loose snow to make a sleeping platform. Use a stick or ski pole to poke an air hole through the roof.

## Snowshoes

Use snowshoes to move over deep snow without sinking. To make snowshoes you need string or cord, and green, bendable branches. Bend a long branch into a loop and tie the ends tightly. Tie on smaller cross-struts, then use cord or string to attach to your boots.

## Snow blindness

Dazzling snow can cause temporary blindness. Wear goggles to protect your eyes. Put sunscreen on exposed skin to prevent sunburn.

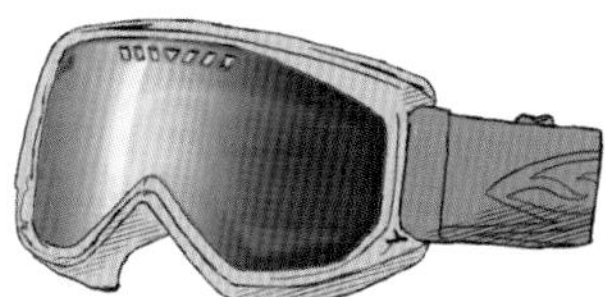

# HAIL, FROST, AND ICE

Hail, frost, and ice are all forms of frozen moisture. Both hailstorms and ice can be deadly, so you have to take great care.

## Hail formation

Hail forms when rising air currents toss ice crystals up and down inside storm clouds. Each time a hailstone rises and falls, new layers of ice are added. Large, heavy hailstones can no longer float, so they crash to the ground.

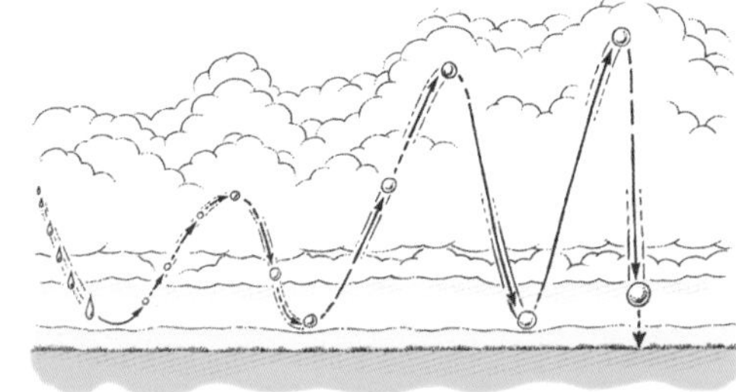

## Hailstones

Most hailstones are no bigger than peas, but they can be as large as golf balls, or even tennis balls. Large, heavy hailstones can shatter car windshields and glass roofs.

## Hoarfrost

Frost forms when moisture condenses on cold surfaces, such as grass, leaves, and glass, and freezes instantly. Thick hoarfrost coats vegetation when temperatures fall well below freezing.

**People have died after being hit by large hailstones. Head for cover. If caught in the open, raise your hands to protect your head.**

## Hidden danger

Ice forms on lakes and ponds when the temperature falls below freezing. Beneath the solid crust is liquid water. Before venturing onto ice, you have to be sure it will bear your weight. Stay away from ice that is less than 4 inches thick.

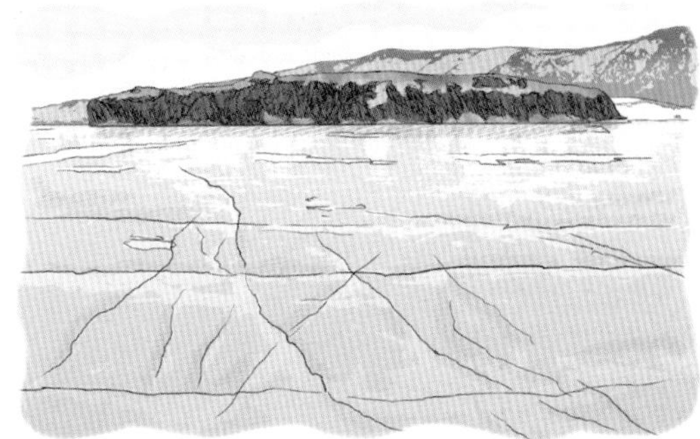

## How to escape from ice

If you fall through ice, brace yourself for the shock of the cold water. Kick up to the surface and keep your head above water. Swim strongly up to the edge, kick your feet, and haul your upper body out. If you have a knife, use it to stab and grip the ice. Heave yourself out. Roll to safety to drain excess water from your clothes and avoid breaking through again.

# COLD CLIMATES

Good preparation is the key to survival in extreme climates. This includes having the right clothing and equipment, but also understanding dangers such as frostbite and how to avoid them.

## Polar and tundra

The Arctic and Antarctic are the coldest places on Earth. South of the Arctic lies the tundra—vast, treeless plains that are snow-covered in winter. In summer the snow melts, revealing boggy, waterlogged ground.

light green shows areas with a northern temperate climate, while dark green shows a temperate climate

## Traditional clothing

Arctic groups, such as the Inuit, traditionally dressed in the skins of the animals they hunted. Undergarments had soft fur next to the skin. Outer garments had fur on the outside to shed snow.

## Modern clothing

Polar explorers wear several layers of clothes made of wool, fleece, or down. Warm air is trapped between layers next to the skin. Sturdy boots, mittens, and a hat or balaclava are also worn.

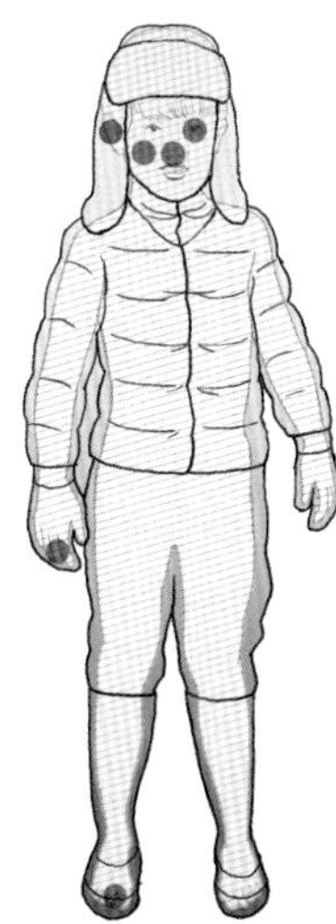

## Frostbite

Frostbite occurs when the skin freezes. Fingers, toes, face, nose, and ears are the areas most at risk of frostbite. Frost-nipped skin looks waxy and feels numb. Wiggle your fingers and toes and stamp your feet to keep the blood flowing. Tuck your hands into your armpits. If in a group, pair off and check one another for signs of frostnip. Warm affected areas slowly. In severe cases, see a doctor.

## Hypothermia

Body temperature can drop dangerously low if a person gets wet or chilled. This is called hypothermia. Early signs are shivering, lack of coordination, and feeling tired and confused. Get to shelter as quickly as possible. Strip off any wet clothes, and wrap the person in a blanket or sleeping bag. Use your body heat to warm them. Supply hot drinks.

## Keep warm

Exercise such as chopping wood will warm you and keep the blood circulating. But avoid overheating—sweat will cool and chill you when you stop.

**BEAR SAYS**

**Avoid sitting on snow, which will wet and chill you. Rest on a log or your rucksack instead.**

# MOUNTAIN CLIMATES

Mountains have different weather than lowlands. For a start, the air is colder. Mountains are wild, windy places where weather conditions change quickly, so you have to be on your guard.

### Thin air

The air high on mountains is less dense and holds less of the sun's heat. The temperature drops 1°F for every 300 ft. of height gain. Thin air also holds less oxygen. Some mountaineers breathe bottled oxygen.

### Gear and clothing

As well as cold- and wet-weather gear, you will need a rope, helmet, and harness if you go climbing. An ice ax and crampons on your boots will help you keep a firm grip on snow and ice.

### Mountain zones

Mountains are found on every continent, including Antarctica. The world's highest mountains are the Himalayas in Asia. The area above 26,000 ft. is called the Death Zone because no one can survive there for long.

## Glaciers

Glaciers form where packed-down snow spills down from the mountains. These frozen "rivers" of ice are cut with deep crevasses. These are particularly dangerous when hidden by fresh snow.

## Fog and mist

Fog and mist are common hazards in mountains (see pages 156–157). Low cloud may hide the summits, or mist may form in valleys when the tops are clear. Come prepared to use a compass.

## Avalanche danger

An avalanche strikes when a mass of snow and ice breaks loose and thunders down a mountain. Avalanches can be triggered by heavy snow, midday heat, skiers, or even loud noises. Beware of deep gullies and steep, snow-covered slopes.

If caught in an avalanche, move your arms and legs in a swimming action to keep at the surface. As the avalanche slows, cup your hands over your mouth to clear a breathing space. Spit to find out which way is up, then try to dig and kick your way to the surface. If this fails, stay calm and wait for help.

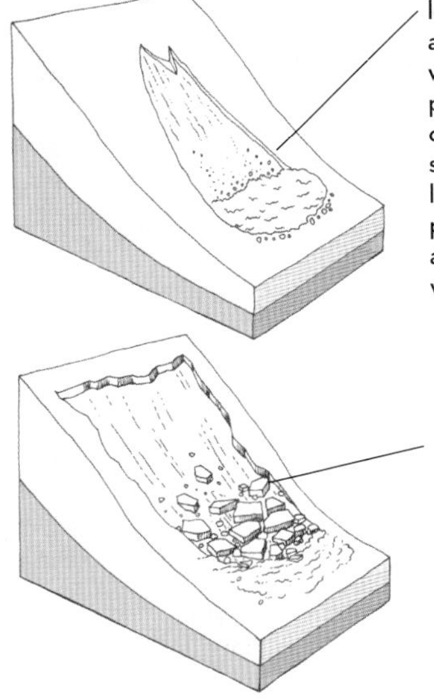

loose snow avalanches occur when light, loose-packed snow lies over a solid base on a steep slope; the top layer will slip from a point, often leaving an inverted "V" where it started

when slab avalanches occur, a whole cohesive layer, or slab, of snow slips as one over softer snow, breaking into smaller blocks

# COASTAL CLIMATES

Coasts generally have a mild, rainy climate. The ocean heats up more slowly than the land, but also cools more slowly. This affects temperatures on land, producing cool summers and warm winters.

## Ocean currents

Ocean currents affect temperatures on nearby land. Warm currents flowing from the tropics warm the land they flow past. Elsewhere, icy polar currents cool nearby coasts.

## Coastal breezes

Coast winds blow in different directions by day and night.

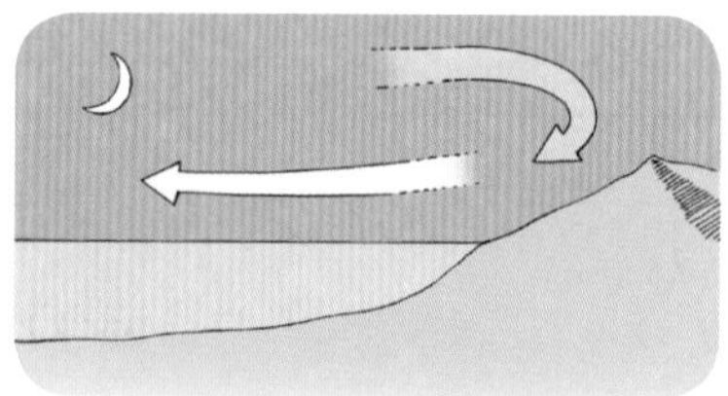

at night, cool air sinks over the land and moves out to sea to replace warmer air that is still rising

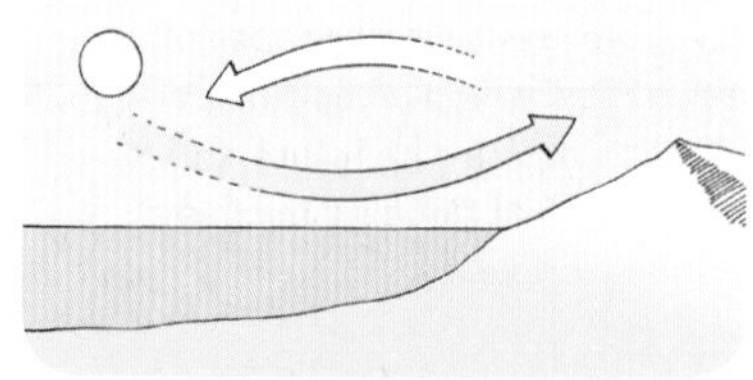

by day, warm air rises off the land and is replaced by cooler air blowing off the sea

## High winds

Coasts are generally breezy places because of on- and offshore winds. This wind-blown tree on a cliff edge shows the direction of the strongest winds, which blow in off the sea.

## Coastal fog

Fog often forms off coasts where warm, moist air makes contact with the cold water surface. Thick fog makes it harder for ships to detect hazards such as shoals and rocks.

## Hurricane damage

Tropical coasts are at risk of hurricanes. In warm, sticky weather, these whirling storms can blow in, wrecking buildings and driving boats onto shore. High seas caused by storm surges can produce floods.

## Rising seas

Sea levels are now rising because of climate change, which is melting polar ice (see page 145). In the future, this will bring added risk of flooding to coasts and islands worldwide.

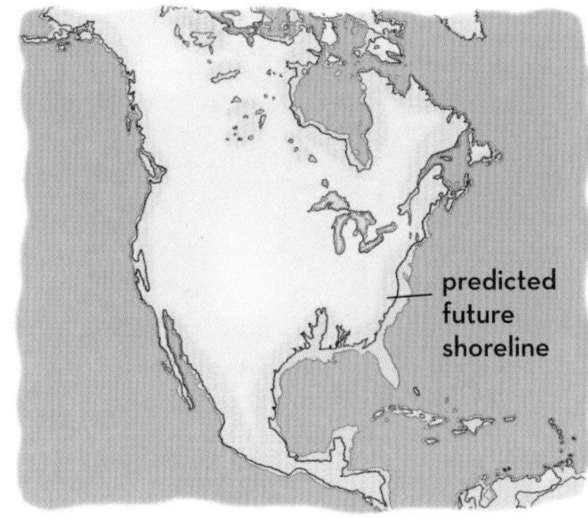

# TROPICAL CLIMATES

Heat can be a serious hazard in the tropics. If the air is moist or humid, it will feel even hotter. Germs and disease thrive in warm climates, so you have to work harder to stay healthy.

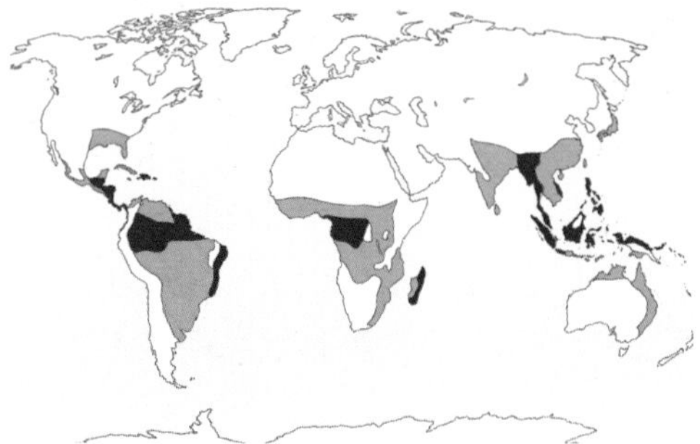

### Tropical regions

Tropical regions north and south of the equator have a hot, humid climate. Rain falls on most days. The high rainfall allows dense rain forests to grow in this zone.

KEY
- tropical forest
- subtropical forest

### Jungle survival

Sleep off the ground, out of reach of creepy-crawlies. Sling your hammock between two trees, and string a tarpaulin above to keep off the rain. Carry dry clothes in a plastic bag and put them on at night. Dry wet clothes by the fire.

### Clothing and equipment

A long-sleeved shirt and pants will help protect you from sunburn and biting insects. Boots guard against leeches and creepy-crawlies. Wear boots when crossing streams. A broad-brimmed hat will keep the sun off. Sunscreen, insect repellent, a map, a compass, and a machete are vital for a jungle trip.

## Prickly heat

This skin irritation is caused by excessive sweating, which chafes the skin and blocks sweat glands. Wash the skin, and put on clean, dry, loose-fitting clothes. Take regular showers if possible.

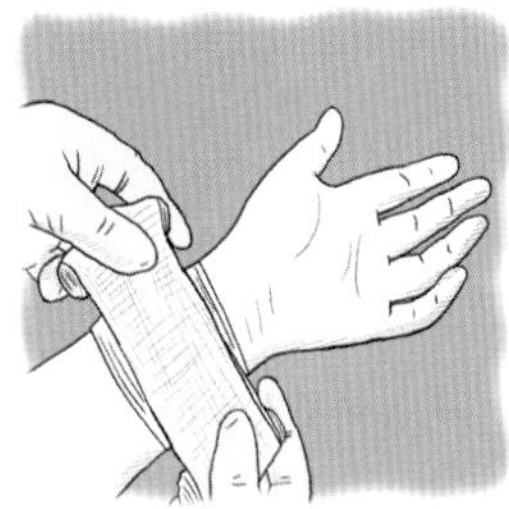

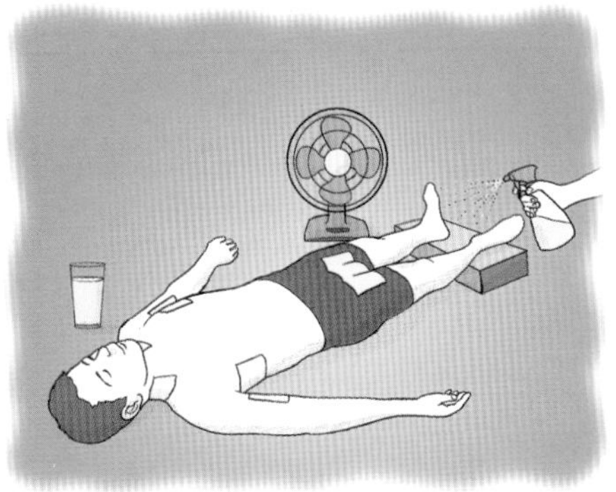

## Treating sunburn

Cool the sunburned area with a cold, wet cloth, or apply calamine lotion. Cover skin or wear complete sunscreen when next in the sun.

## Heatstroke

Heatstroke is when your body overheats and natural cooling systems fail. See page 102 for details on how to treat this.

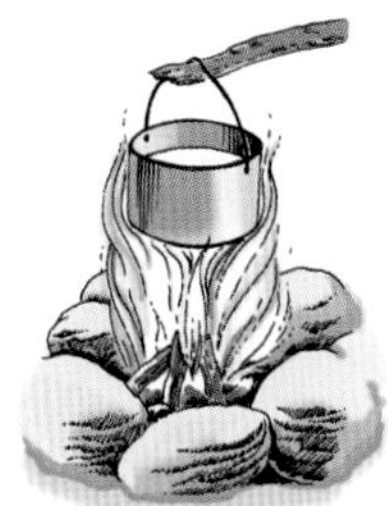

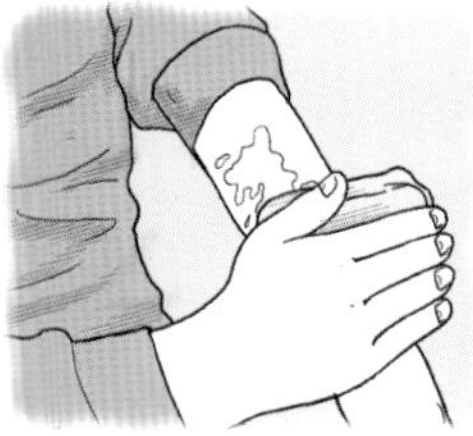

## Purify water

Bacteria thrive in hot, damp climates. Boil water for 15 minutes or sterilize with purifying tablets.

## Sterilize wounds

Cuts and scratches can quickly become infected. Sterilize all wounds with antiseptic ointment or wipes.

## Rest in the shade

Don't rest in full sun. Rig a cloth or tarpaulin to provide yourself with shade.

# DRY CLIMATES

Water is the body's main need. You can last for weeks without food, if necessary, but only a few days without water. Finding water is the top priority for desert survival. Rest in the shade by day to reduce water loss through sweating. Work or walk at night, when it is cooler. Avoid strenuous activity that will make you sweat.

## Deserts

Deserts are places where less than 10 inches of rain falls in a year. Most deserts lie in a belt 15–30° north and south of the equator. Warm, dry air sinking in these zones prevents rain clouds from forming. Deserts may be hot by day, but temperatures drop steeply at night.

KEY

desert areas

## Vital water

You need to drink at least 2 liters of water a day to replace body fluids. In dry climates and survival situations, this can rise to 5–6 liters. If you don't drink enough you will become dehydrated. As well as feeling thirsty, you could get a headache and feel sick, confused, and drowsy. If water is scarce, take small sips rather than gulps.

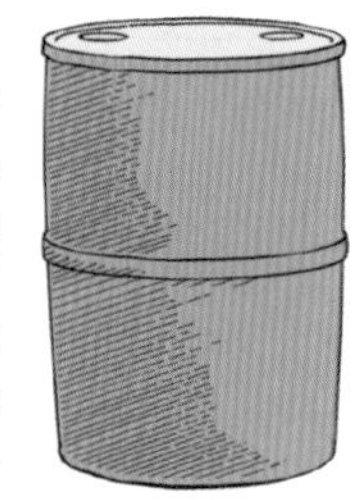

## Desert shelter

Dig a shallow trench and cover it with a sheet or tarpaulin. Use stones to weight the edges. If possible, rig two layers of cloth, with an air space in between.

## Clothing and gear

Wear thin, loose-fitting clothing and keep covered. Light-colored clothing reflects sunlight while dark colors absorb it. A wide-brimmed hat protects the back of the neck. Sunscreen and sunglasses are a must, along with stout boots to ward off snakes and scorpions.

## Where to look for water

Dig for water in the lowest part of a dry stream or river bed. Green plants show where water seeps down cliff faces or trickles underground. Animal tracks may lead to water, while prickly pears and some types of cactus provide liquid.

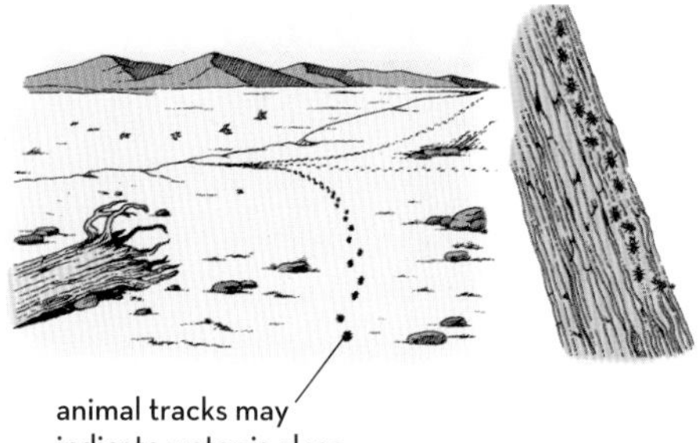


## Sand and dust storms

High winds whip up dust storms, which fill the air with sand or grit. Wear goggles and a face mask if you have them, or wrap a cloth around your head and cover your eyes, nose, and mouth. Head for shelter such as a car, tent, or rocks.

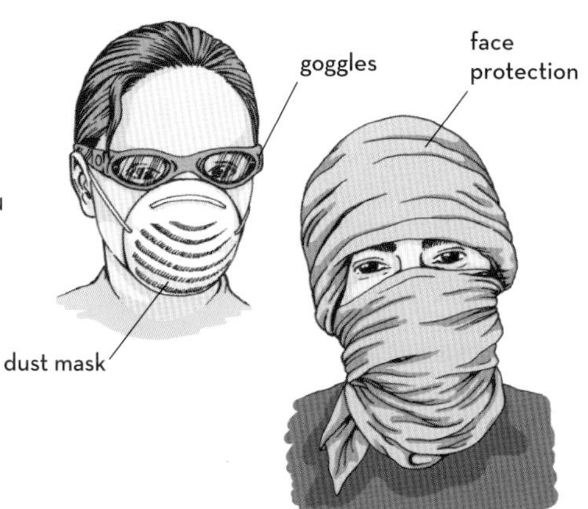

# WEATHER FORECASTING

Knowing what the weather will bring is useful for anyone who spends time outdoors. Checking the forecast is a vital part of planning for all outdoor expeditions.

## Weather stations and aircraft

Weather stations all over the world provide data on temperatures, cloud cover, winds, and rainfall. Aircraft and weather balloons gather data about conditions high in the air.

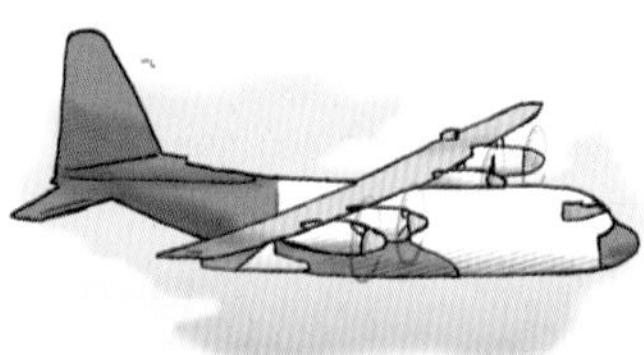

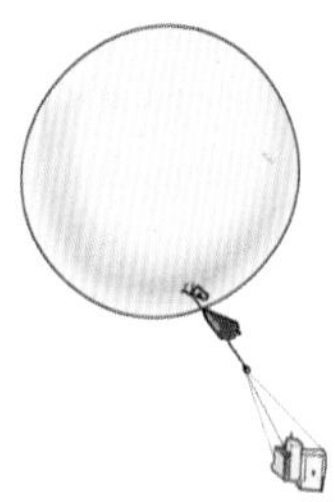

## Satellites

Satellites use radar and other sensing equipment to track clouds, storms, and hurricanes. This helps experts to predict which way storms are moving, so they can issue warnings.

## Weather buoys

Weather ships and buoys provide information about conditions at sea, such as wind and waves. This is used for land and shipping forecasts.

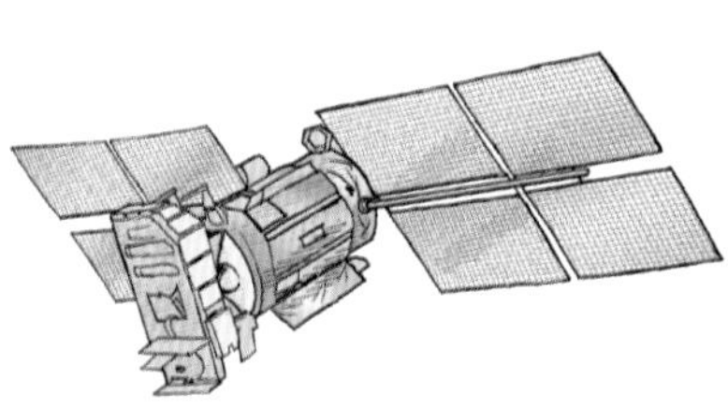

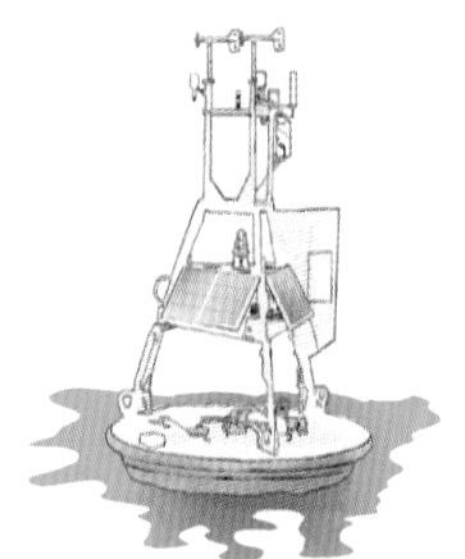

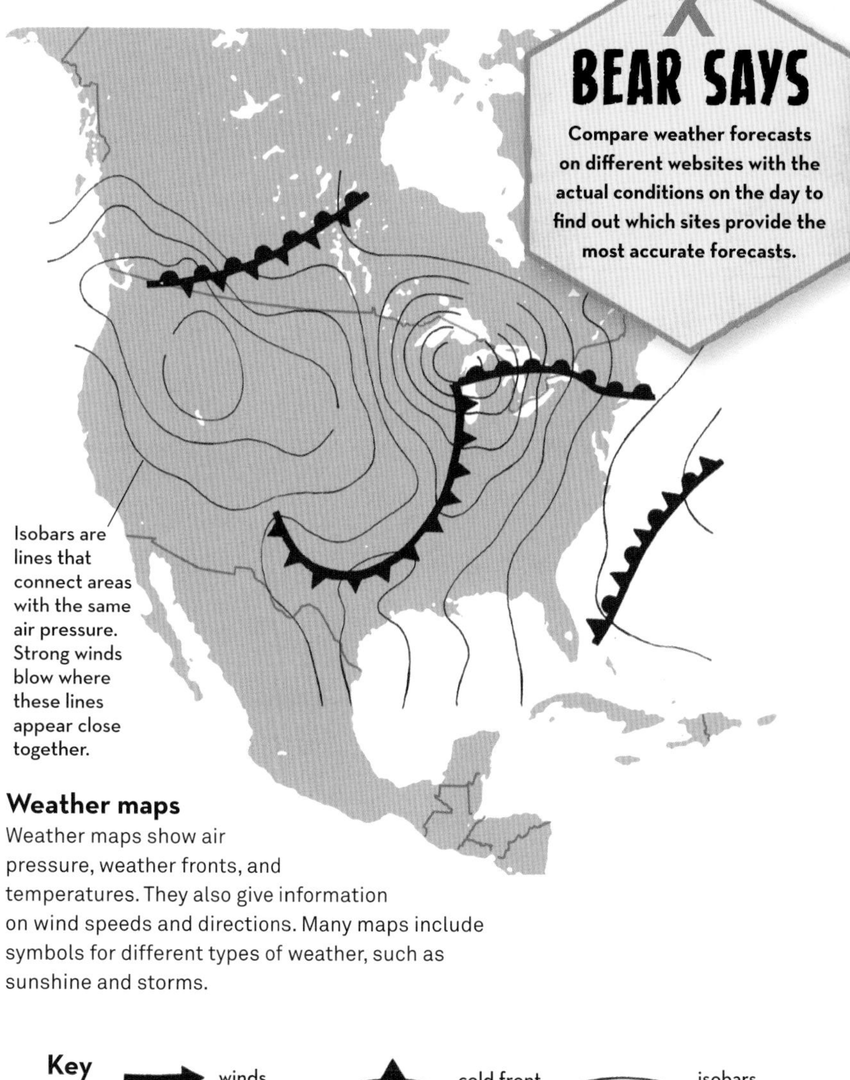

## BEAR SAYS

**Compare weather forecasts on different websites with the actual conditions on the day to find out which sites provide the most accurate forecasts.**

Isobars are lines that connect areas with the same air pressure. Strong winds blow where these lines appear close together.

## Weather maps

Weather maps show air pressure, weather fronts, and temperatures. They also give information on wind speeds and directions. Many maps include symbols for different types of weather, such as sunshine and storms.

**Key**

winds

warm front

cold front

occluded front

isobars

stationary front

# WEATHER RECORDS

What are the Earth's hottest, coldest, windiest, and wettest places? This map shows the locations of the world's most extreme weather, based on records that go back over 150 years.

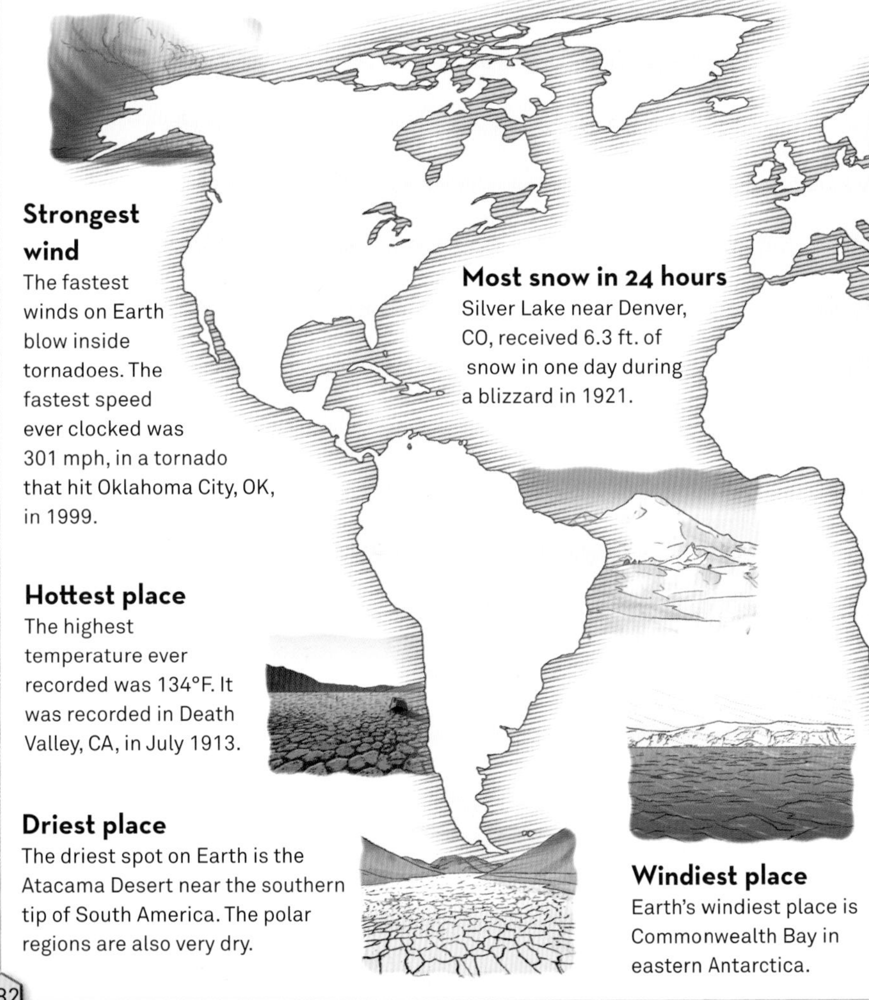

**Strongest wind**
The fastest winds on Earth blow inside tornadoes. The fastest speed ever clocked was 301 mph, in a tornado that hit Oklahoma City, OK, in 1999.

**Most snow in 24 hours**
Silver Lake near Denver, CO, received 6.3 ft. of snow in one day during a blizzard in 1921.

**Hottest place**
The highest temperature ever recorded was 134°F. It was recorded in Death Valley, CA, in July 1913.

**Driest place**
The driest spot on Earth is the Atacama Desert near the southern tip of South America. The polar regions are also very dry.

**Windiest place**
Earth's windiest place is Commonwealth Bay in eastern Antarctica.

## Highest annual rainfall

The town of Cherrapunji in northern India recorded 1,042 inches of rain in 1860–61. The nearby town of Mawsynram holds the modern record, receiving up to 467 inches of rain per year.

## BEAR SAYS

**Weather records are updated constantly. Make sure your research is up to date when planning a trip.**

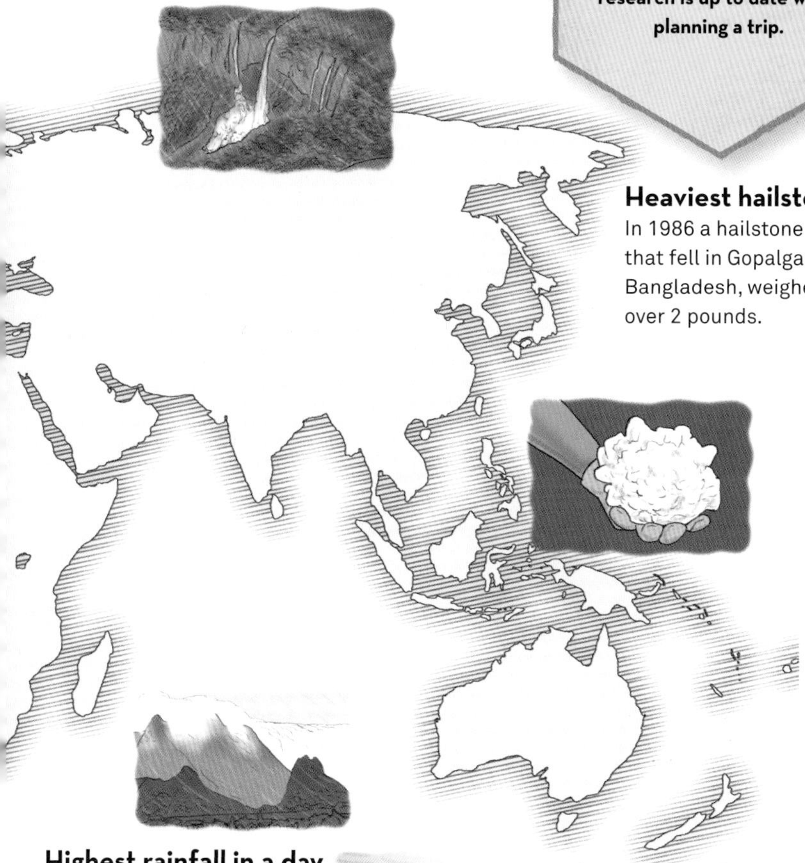

## Heaviest hailstone

In 1986 a hailstone that fell in Gopalganj, Bangladesh, weighed over 2 pounds.

## Highest rainfall in a day

Foc-Foc on the island of Reunion in the Indian Ocean received 72 inches of rain in 24 hours during a hurricane in 1966.

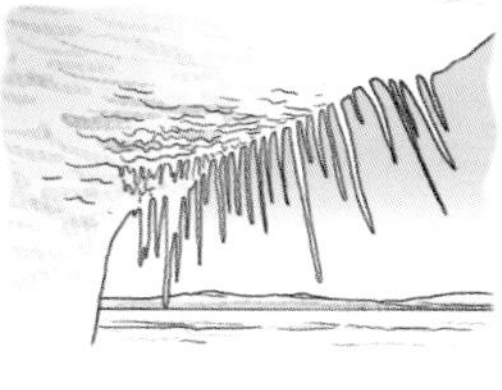

## Coldest place

The coldest temperature ever recorded at ground level was -128.5°F. It was recorded at Vostock Base in Antarctica.

# INDEX

## D



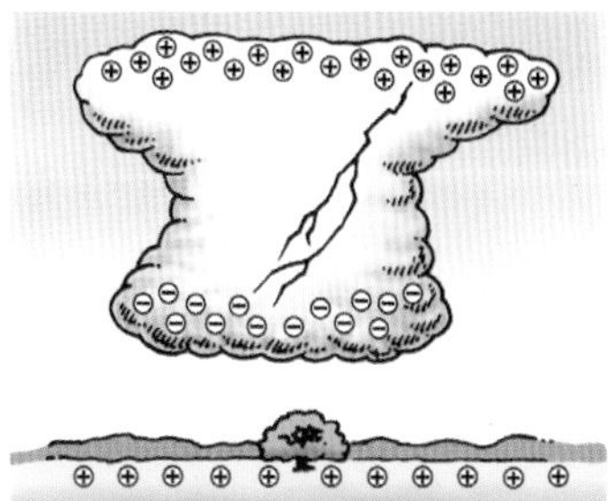



## E

## K



## L



## M

## T

## U



## V



## W

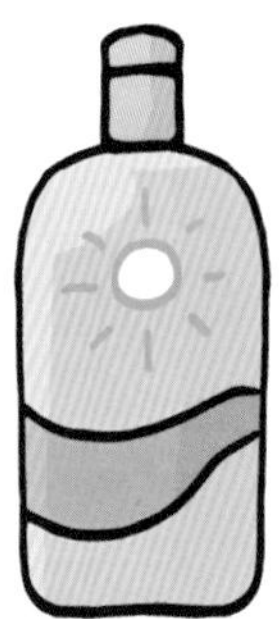